Revised

Practice in Music Theory

Josephine Koh

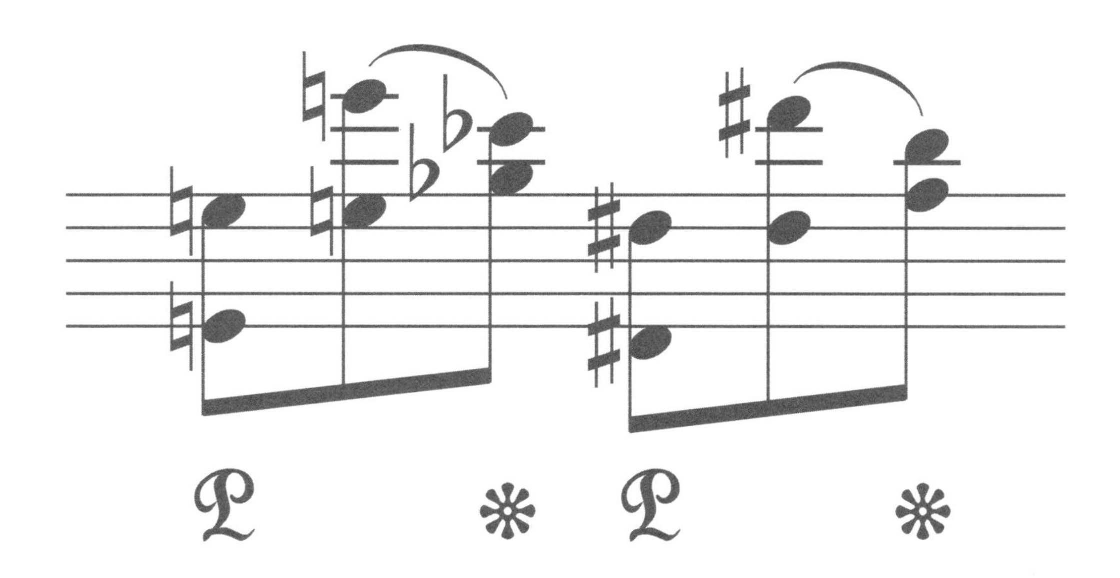

Grade 8

Based on the music theory syllabus of the Associated Board of the Royal Schools of Music

Published by
Wells Music Publishers
896 Dunearn Road,
Sime Darby Centre
#04-03
Singapore 589472

ISBN 981-05-6613-1

First edition published in 2000 © by Music Plaza Pte Ltd
Second edition published in 2007 © by Wells Music Publishers

Cover design by Lee Kowling
Typesetting by Joni Tan

For the completion of this series, I owe much to my family members who have patiently shared my ten years of preoccupations and deprivations. I would like to thank all those close friends for their words of comfort and encouragement and all music teachers who have offered their invaluable suggestions.

Josephine Koh
January 2000

The underlying function of harmony is to express emotion... a concept founded on an instinctive awareness of what might be terms the Tonal Spectrum.

Antony Hopkins

I have perused Practice in Music Theory Grade 8 with great interest. The presentation is musically sound in all aspects and this text will be of invaluable assistance to serious musicians as well as students taking music examinations.

Mr Paul Abisheganaden M.B.E.
Singapore Cultural Medallion Awardee
Senior Fellow Centre for the Arts,
National University of Singapore

Contents

Understanding Chromatic Harmony

Evolution of Dissonances and Chromatic Chords

- Up till the 19th century, composers used chromatic notes to vary and enrich their basically diatonic harmonic progressions in their compositions.
- Dissonant notes were used mainly as part-movement, introduced for decorative purposes, such as the passing note, suspension or appoggiatura.
- Over time with the development of more advanced harmonic colours, these dissonant notes came to be accepted and thus new, free-standing chromatic chords were formed and established.
- Still, in the common practice period, dissonances were resolved; sometimes delayed, decorated, or implied.
- By the late 19th century, however, the extensive use of chromaticism and intense dissonances threatened the established tonal system. Dissonances became independent of harmony and were much used with liberation. Eventually, with the emergence of new compositional styles in the early 20th century, the concept of tonality and traditional harmony gave way to many revolutionary approaches that changed the musical world.

Types of Chromatic Chords

The following forms a list of the most commonly used chromatic chords found in the music of the common practice period.

1. *The Neapolitan 6th*

   Derived from the supertonic chord, it has its root chromatically lowered. A major chord is thus formed in the first inversion. It is commonly notated:

   C: ♭IIb

2. *The Diminished 7th*

   Derived from the leading-note seventh (vii°^{7}) in the minor key, it is a chromatic chord in the major key. It is usually used with much freedom to enhance the harmonic colour in a passage. Notated:

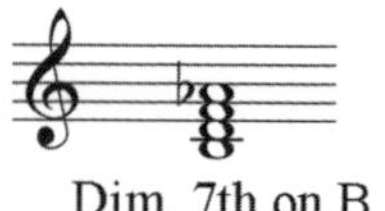

Dim. 7th on B

3. *The Augmented 6th chords*

   Known as the Italian, French or German 6ths, these chords contain the characteristic interval of an augmented 6th found between the bass note and an upper part (see pages 5 and 6).

4. *Borrowed Chords*

   These chords are simply "borrowed" from the minor key or vice versa for a modal or novel flavour. They are commonly notated in Roman numerals according to the quality and position of the chords (see pages 11 and 12).

5. *Altered Chords*

   Chromatic alterations are made to these chords to form a different quality, such as the augmented dominant triad (V$^+$) or the chromatic supertonic 7th (II^7) (see pages 14 and 15).

6. *Secondary Dominants*

   Chromatic alterations to chords, can result in the formation of secondary dominant harmonies. These secondary dominant harmonies are seen as temporary or suggested modulations. Notated as V$^{(7)}$ of another chord, the relationship is identified by the chord symbol that follows. Thus

   C: II^7 or V^7/V

Note: *Details of these chords are found in Practice in Music Theory Grade 7 or in the subsequent topics of this book.*

Modulations

Chromatic chords are frequently used as pivot chords in the modulatory process. Notes may sometimes be *enharmonically written* to enable smooth and effective part-movement which leads into the new key. These pivot chords may be diatonic in one key but chromatic in the other or chromatic in both keys. An established cadence however, is necessary to confirm a modulation. (See page 12, example 2.)

Harmonic Analysis

The Extended Roman symbols are highly recommended for use in harmonic analysis. However, you may also use words in your description, particularly for the Diminished 7ths, Neapolitan 6th and Augmented 6th chords. Some intensely chromatic passages use pedal points, lasting from one or two to several beats. The pedal notes are best indicated with a horizontal line. Chordal progressions above the pedal should be effective when the pedal is removed.

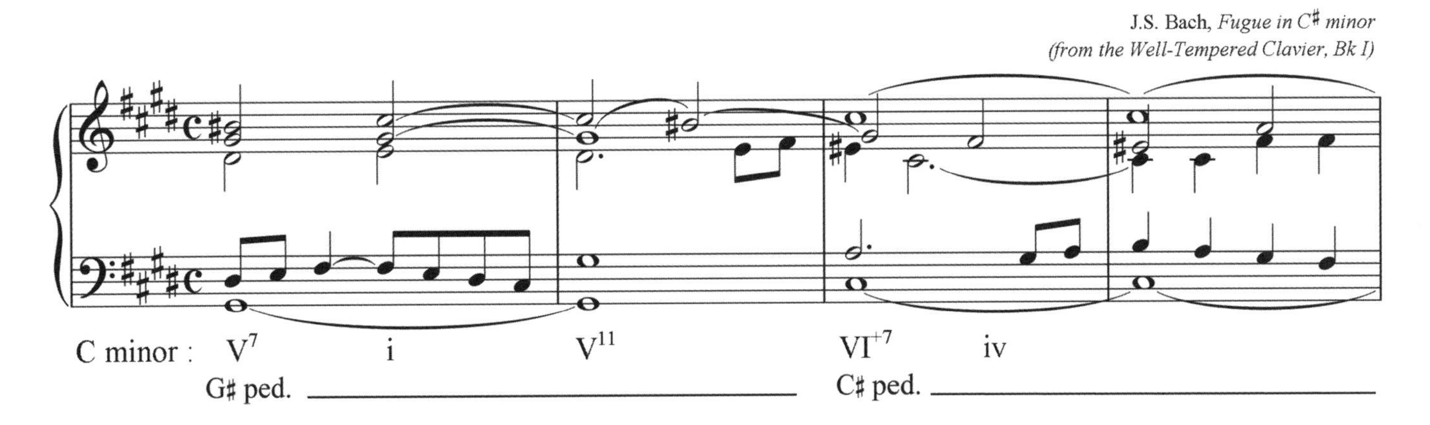

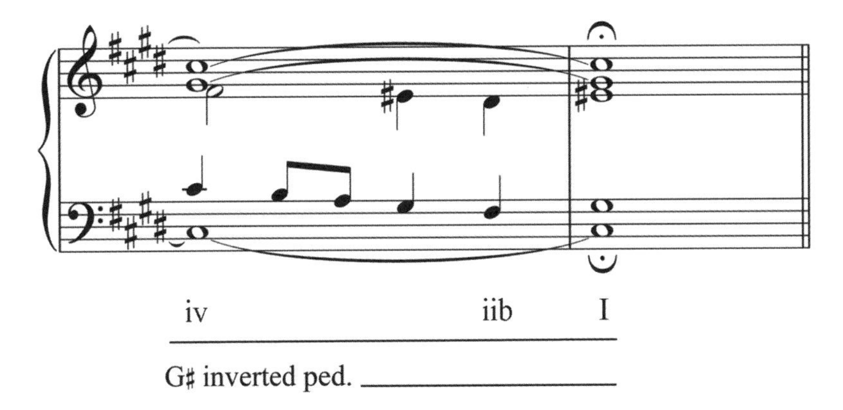

The purpose of harmonic analysis should not be seen as an end in itself, but as an attempt to simplify and understand the harmonic language and vocabulary used in the era of tonal music.

Section I

Advanced Harmonic Vocabulary

Extension of the Triad & Chromatic Chords

Diatonic Dominant Discords: V^9, V^{11} and V^{13}

Superimposing intervals of a 3rd above a basic triad results in extensions of the triad; forming not only 7th chords but also chords of the 9th, 11th and 13th. The most common extensions occur on the dominant triad.

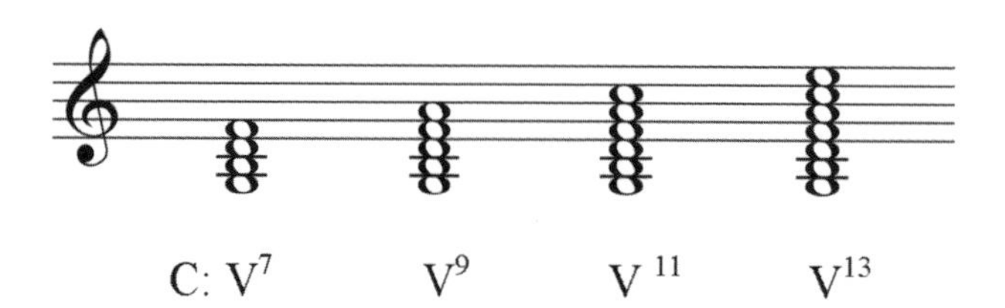

However, not all the notes are used in instrumental music of the common practice period. Usually one or more notes may be omitted, which may reduce the texture to not more than 4 actual parts.

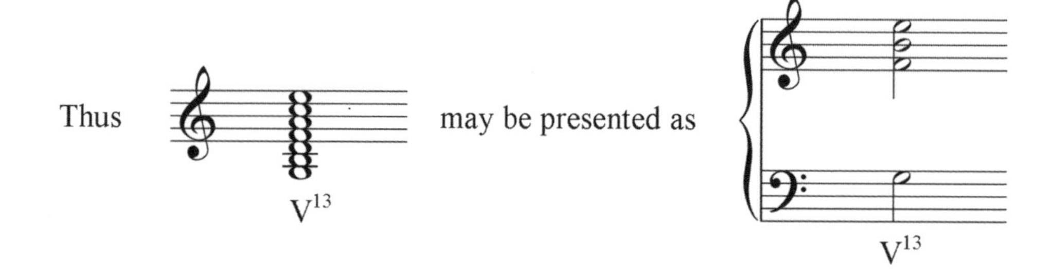

The Dominant Minor 9th

It is a **chromatic** chord in the **major** key.
It is a **diatonic** chord in the **minor** key.
The dominant minor 9th is more discordant than the major 9th.

Compare the following:

Treatment

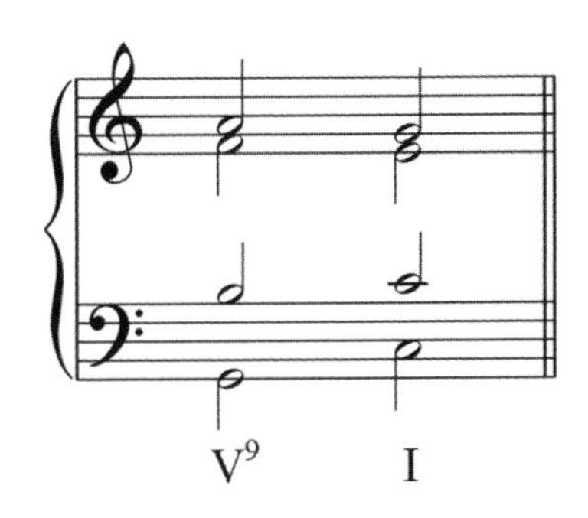

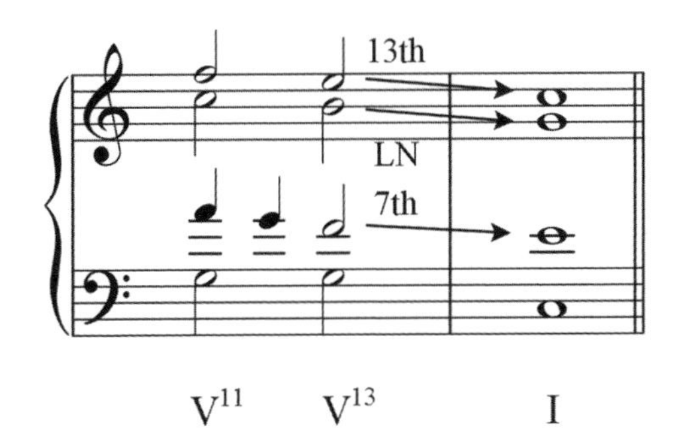

a) Both the V^9 and V^{13} resolve to I.
V^{11} usually progresses to another dominant chord (i.e. V, V^9 or V^{13}) before progressing to I for a satisfactory cadence to be attained.

b) The 7th, 9th, 11th and 13th resolve accordingly, usually by step down.
The leading note (LN) raises to the tonic or falls a 3rd.

Musical Examples

1. The dominant minor 9th enriches the passage, sounding more colourful, intense and expressive than the V and V^7 chords.

Beethoven, *Piano Concerto No. 3*

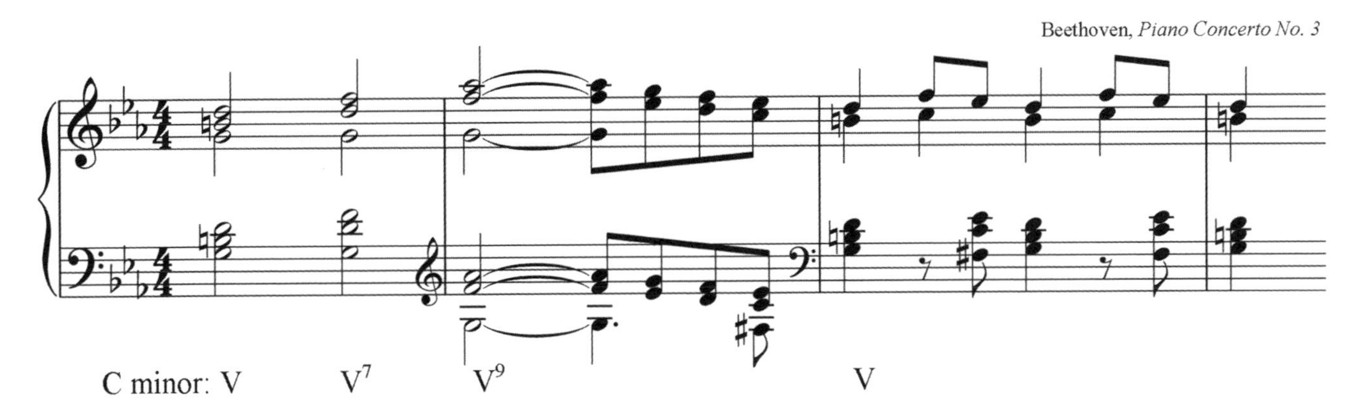

2. The V^{11} is played as an arpeggio over the dominant pedal note.

3. Often a 9th, 11th or 13th added to a dominant chord functions as an embellishment – an appoggiatura, a passing note or a changing note.
In harmonic analysis, the student is expected to include such notes in the description, unless they are insignificant or of very short duration.

*Here, the 13th note is introduced as an anticipation before the resolution.

4. The V^9 is used here as a secondary dominant.

Augmented Sixth Chords

Definition

There are three versions of the **augmented sixth chord**: *Italian 6th, French 6th and German 6th.*

Common to these chords is the strongly dissonant, harmonic interval – the augmented 6th created by:

- the submediant in the bass (flattened in the major key), with
- the raised subdominant in an upper part

The *tonic note* is also present in all three chords.

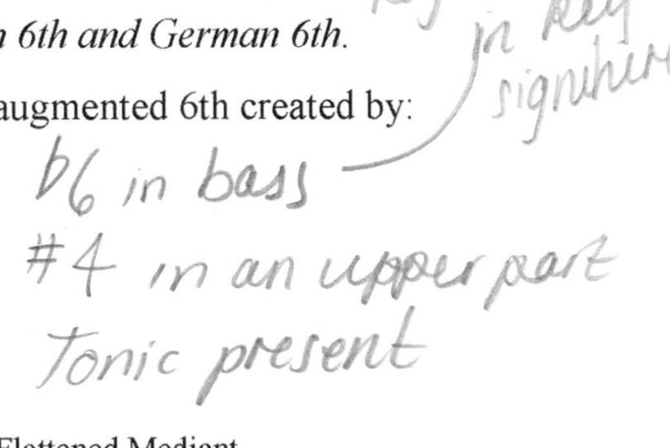

Play these chords in C major:

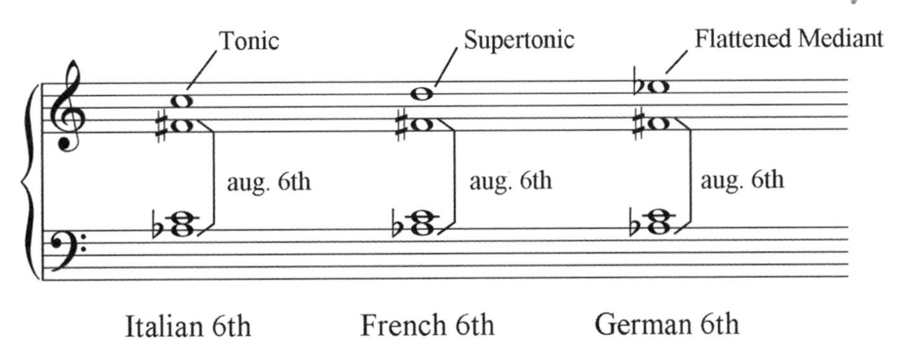

Italian 6th French 6th German 6th

Sounding similarly in C minor:

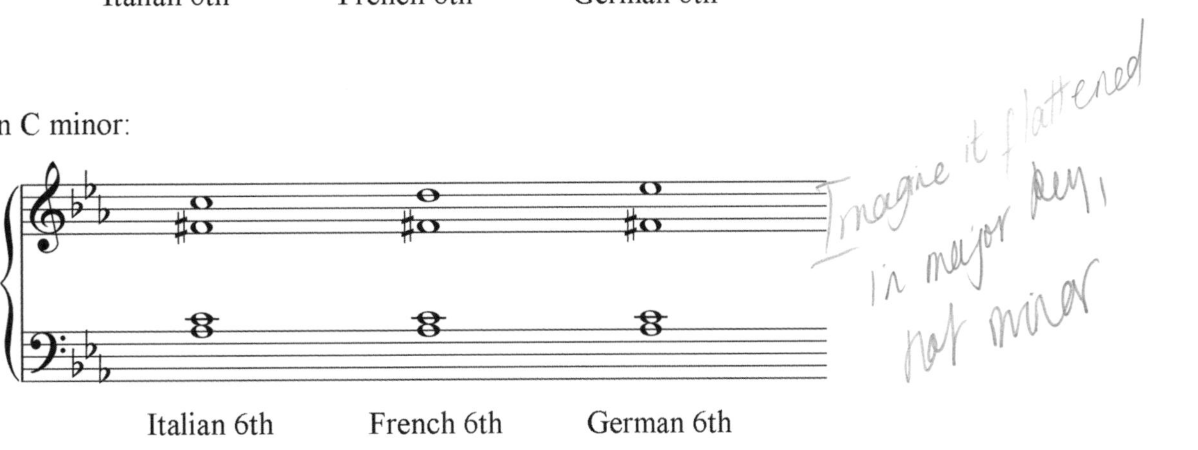

Italian 6th French 6th German 6th

Resolution

The dissonant interval and chromatic notes require resolution. Normally, the augmented 6th moves towards an octave – the sharpened note *raises* and the flattened note *falls*.

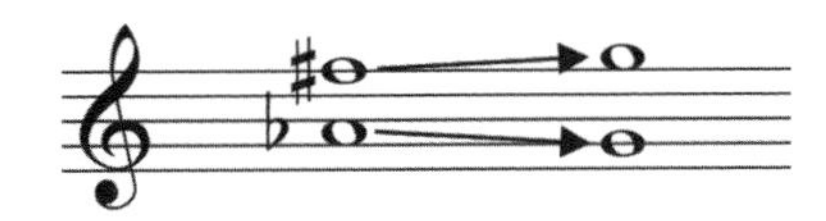

The regular resolution of the augmented 6th chords is to V or sometimes Ic.

The parallel 5th is unavoidable and permitted

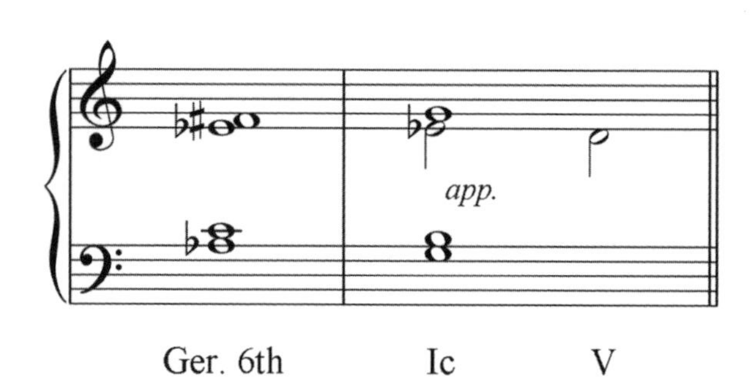

1. Write the Italian, French and German augmented 6th chords in the following keys. The first example has been shown.

2. Identify the following augmented 6th chords. Indicate each as an Italian 6th (It. 6th), German 6th (Ger. 6th), or French 6th (Fr. 6th). State the prevailing key at the beginning. The first example has been shown.

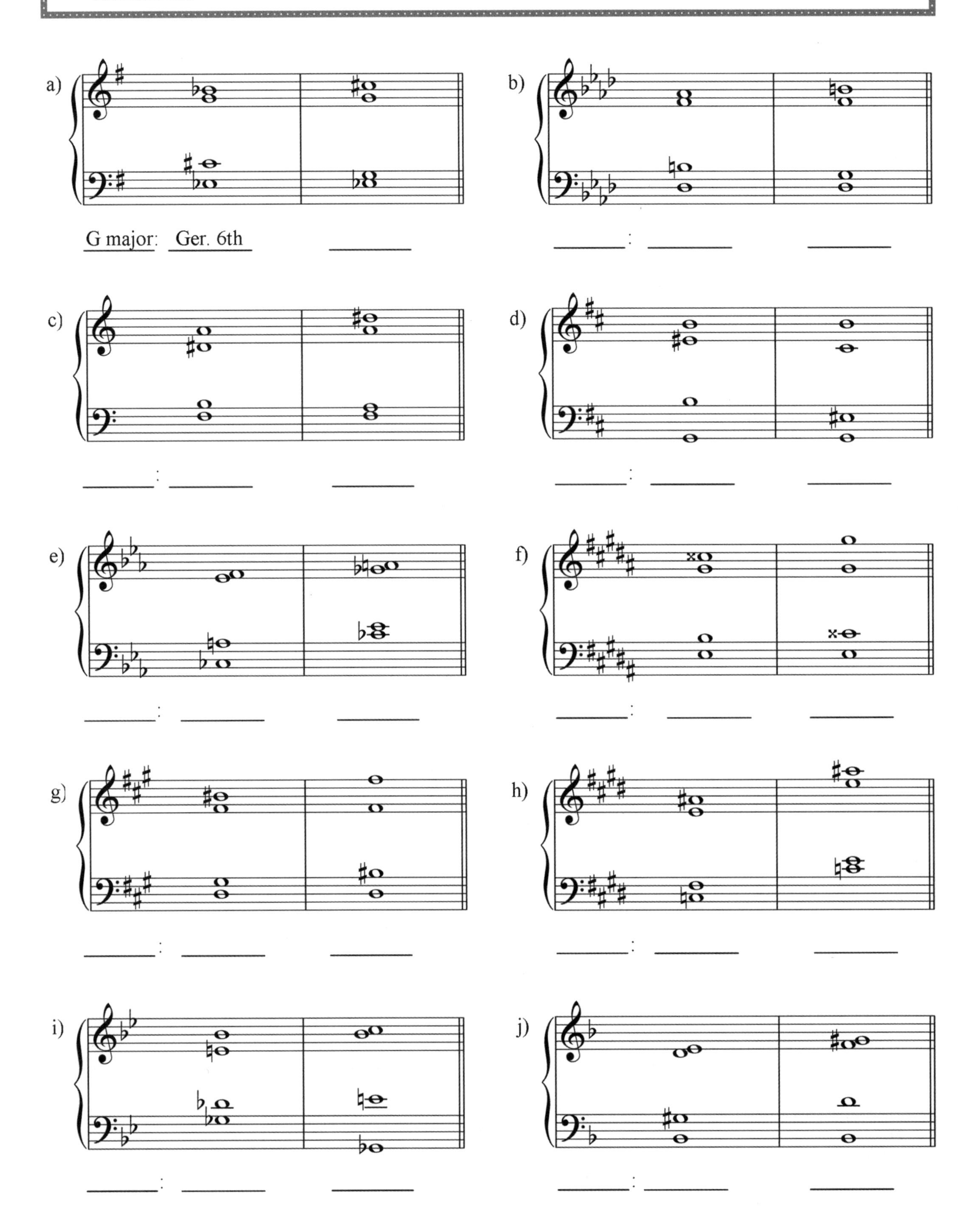

3. Complete the following exercise by writing the notes of the chords or by naming them. Also state the keys in (c) and (e).

a)

F major: French 6th ___________ ___________

b)

G minor: ___________ German 6th ___________

c)

_________: ___________ ___________ German 6th

d)

A♭ major: Italian 6th French 6th ___________

e)

_________: ___________ Italian 6th German 6th

Musical Examples

1. The Italian 6th provides harmonic richness towards the cadence leading into C major.

2. Augmented 6th chords may sometimes function as pivot chords resolving effectively into a foreign key.

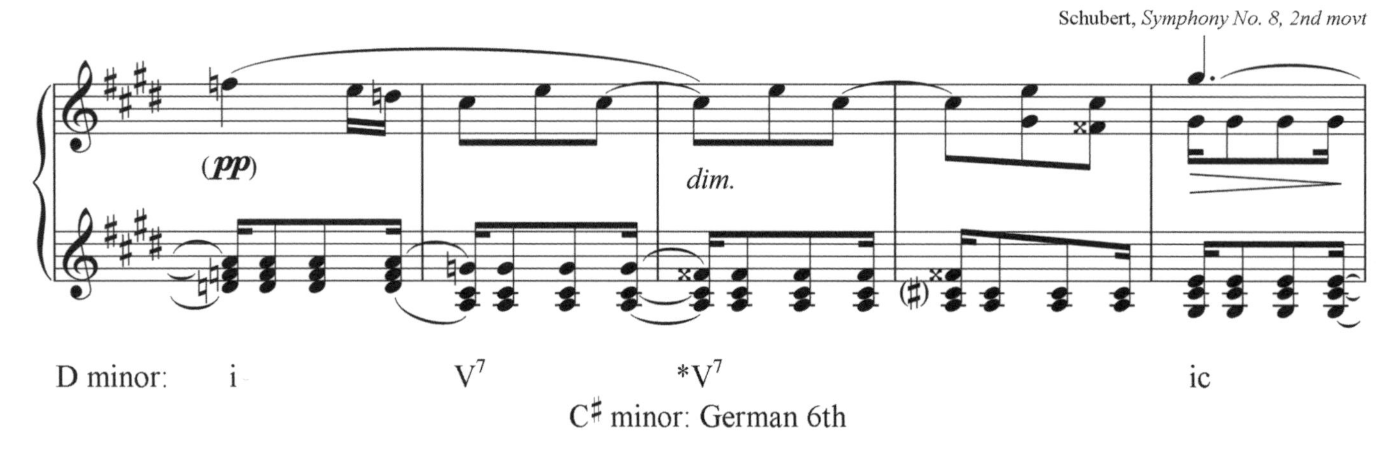

*The V^7 in D minor is enharmonically written. It serves as a pivot chord modulating to C♯ minor.

4. Can you locate the French augmented 6th chord followed by a dominant chord in the extract below?

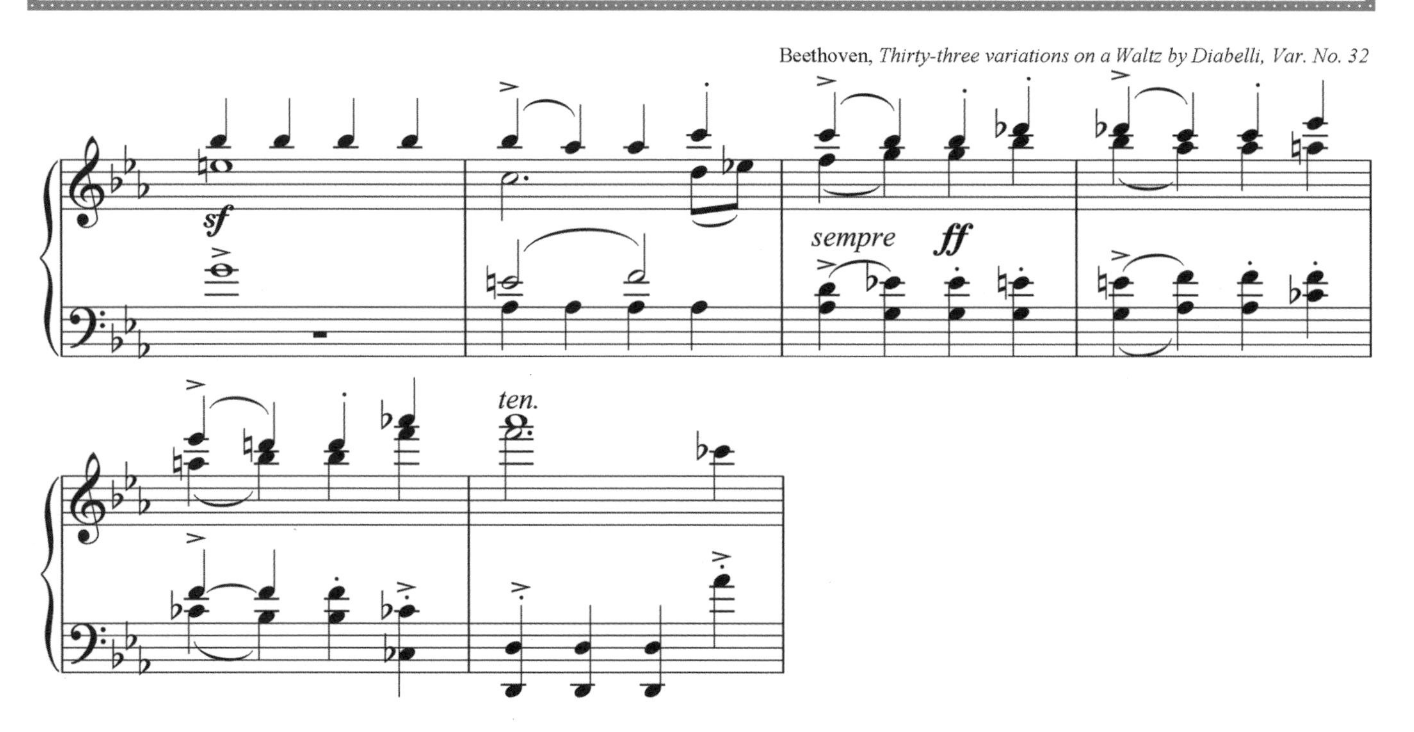

Borrowed Chords and Altered Chords

Borrowed Chords

Study the harmonies of the two extracts below.

Notice that the E major triad shifts to the E minor mode in bars 9 to 10.

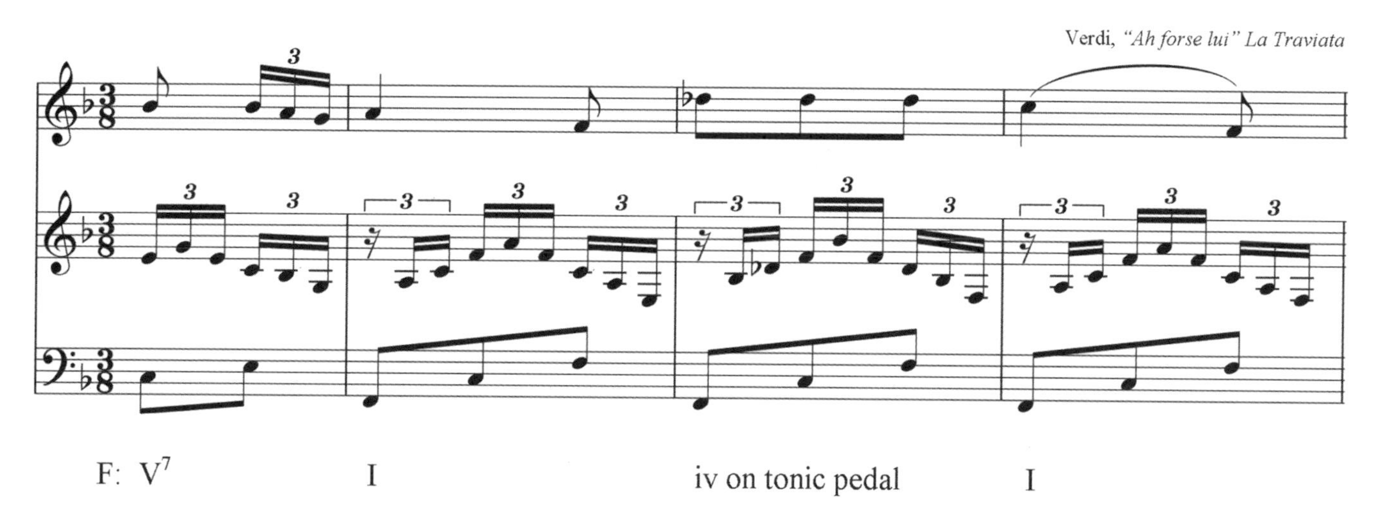

The chord, iv, is a minor triad. It is said to be *borrowed* from the key of F minor.

Definition

Music written in the major key may borrow chords from the parallel minor key. These are called **borrowed chords**. The presence of accidentals or chromatic notes does not imply any modulation and should not be confused with the other chromatic chords studied thus far.

Compare the chords in C major and C minor.

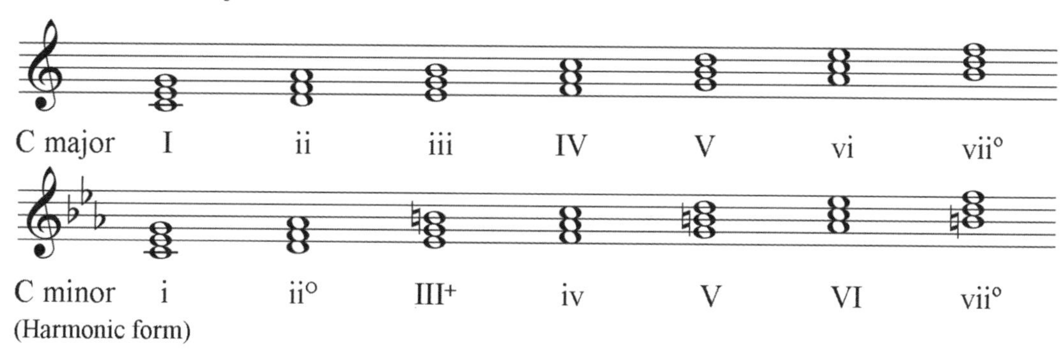

Except for the dominant chord (V) and leading note chord (vii°), the qualities of the triads in the harmonic minor key are notably different from those in the major key. Composers from the time of Beethoven onwards began to borrow chords from the parallel minor key, which led to further expansion and exploitation of the range of harmonic possibilities.

By borrowing chords from C harmonic minor, the availability of chords in C major is extended to include:

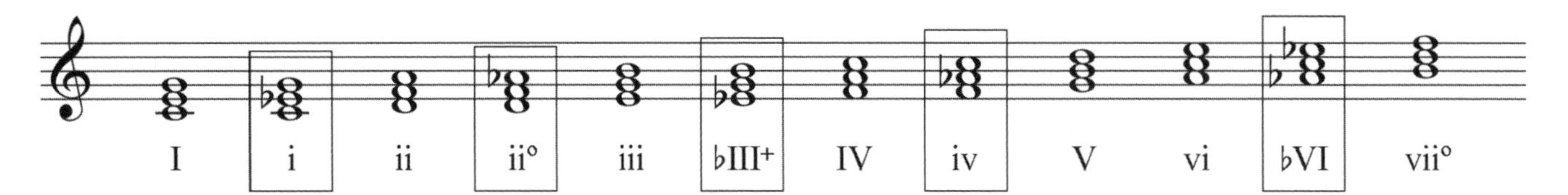

In similar light, many alternatives are possible, arising from the 6th and 7th degrees of the melodic minor scale.

Musical Examples

1. It is rare for music in the minor key to borrow chords from the major key, except in works which end with a *tierce de Picardie** – a tonic major chord.

2. In the following example, the tonic major chord is used to introduce a modulation from the minor key to its tonic major.

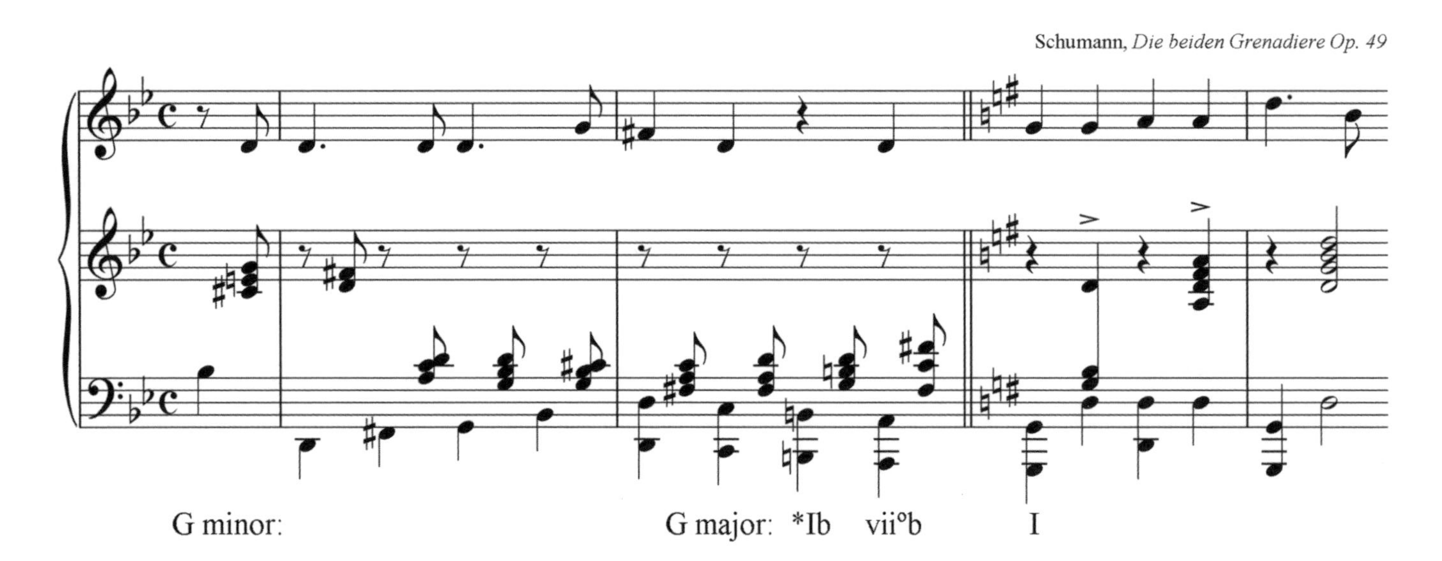

Method of Notation

It is relatively simple to notate borrowed chords using the **Extended Roman Method**. *See Practice in Music Theory Grade 7, Introduction (ii)*

Thus the chords which can be borrowed from C melodic minor include:

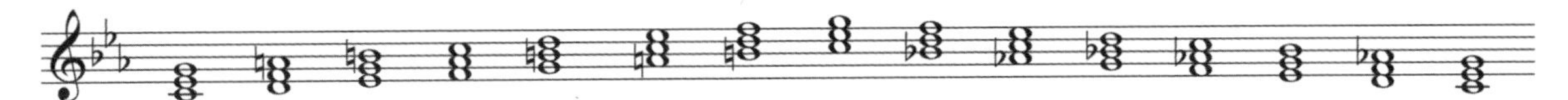

In C major, the chords are notated:

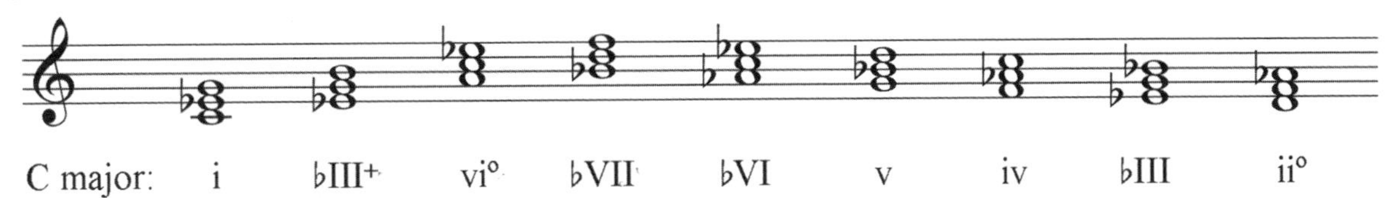

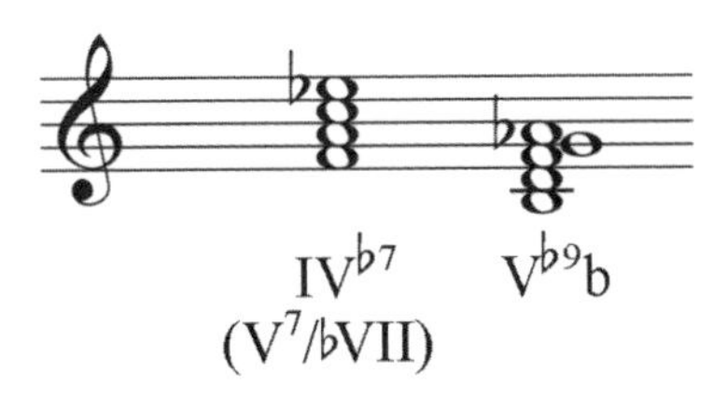

5. Can you find two diminished 7th chords, a borrowed chord and a secondary dominant chord in the passage below?

Altered Chords

Definition

Diatonic chords may be altered by accidentals to form chromatic chords known as altered chords.

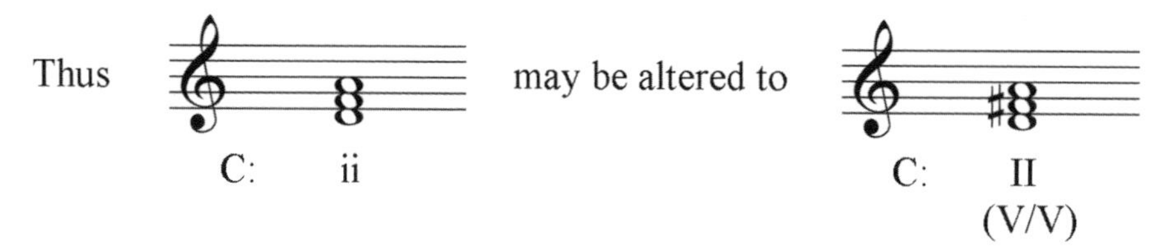

The notation may be known as II or alternatively as V/V, the latter serves the function of a *secondary dominant*. In the next example,

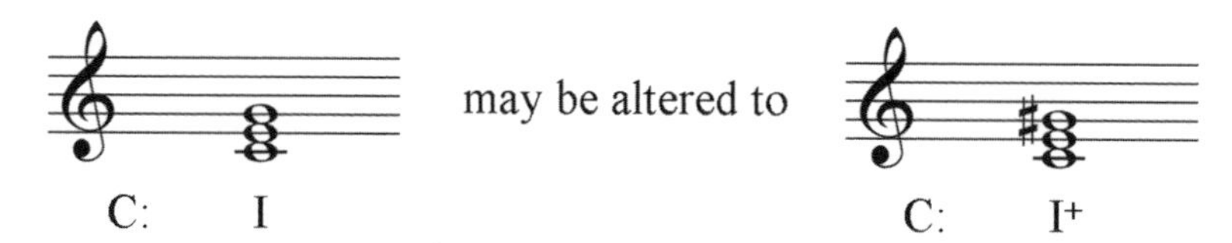

The quality and nature of the chord thus change from a major to an augmented chord.

Play the passage below:

The strongly expressive effect of both altered chromatic discords* is apparent within the extract. The V^7/iii, a secondary dominant, is quickly resolved upon the next bar.

More Examples

Any diatonic chord may be altered to become chromatic.

a) For example:

C: IV

may be altered and becomes:

b) Augmented triads can be formed by raising the 5th note of a major triad. Most commonly found are:

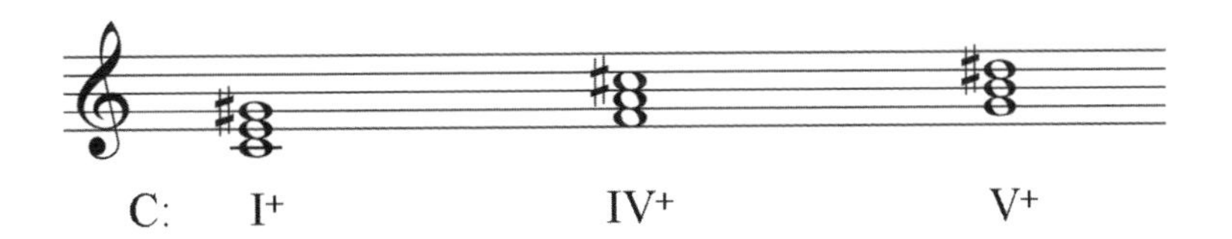

c) A diatonic triad or seventh chord may be altered by adding accidentals. For example:

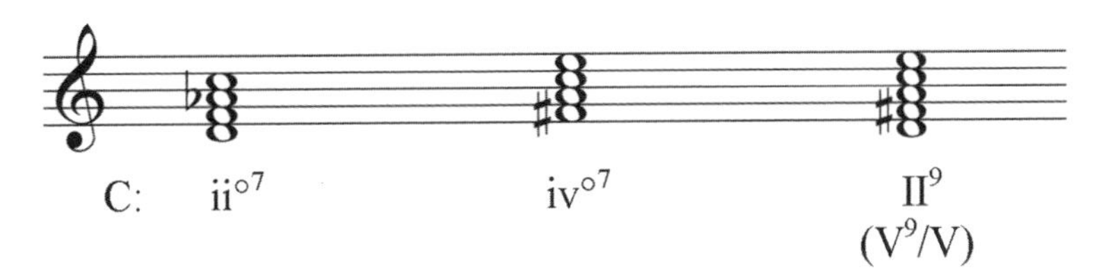

d) Altered chords may also function like secondary dominants. Thus,

*Chromatically altered chord

6. Provide harmonic analysis for the following extracts using Extended Roman Notation. You may write, in words, chords of the Neapolitan 6th, Augmented 6th and Diminished 7th. Show the length of the pedal note, where it occurs, with a horizontal line.

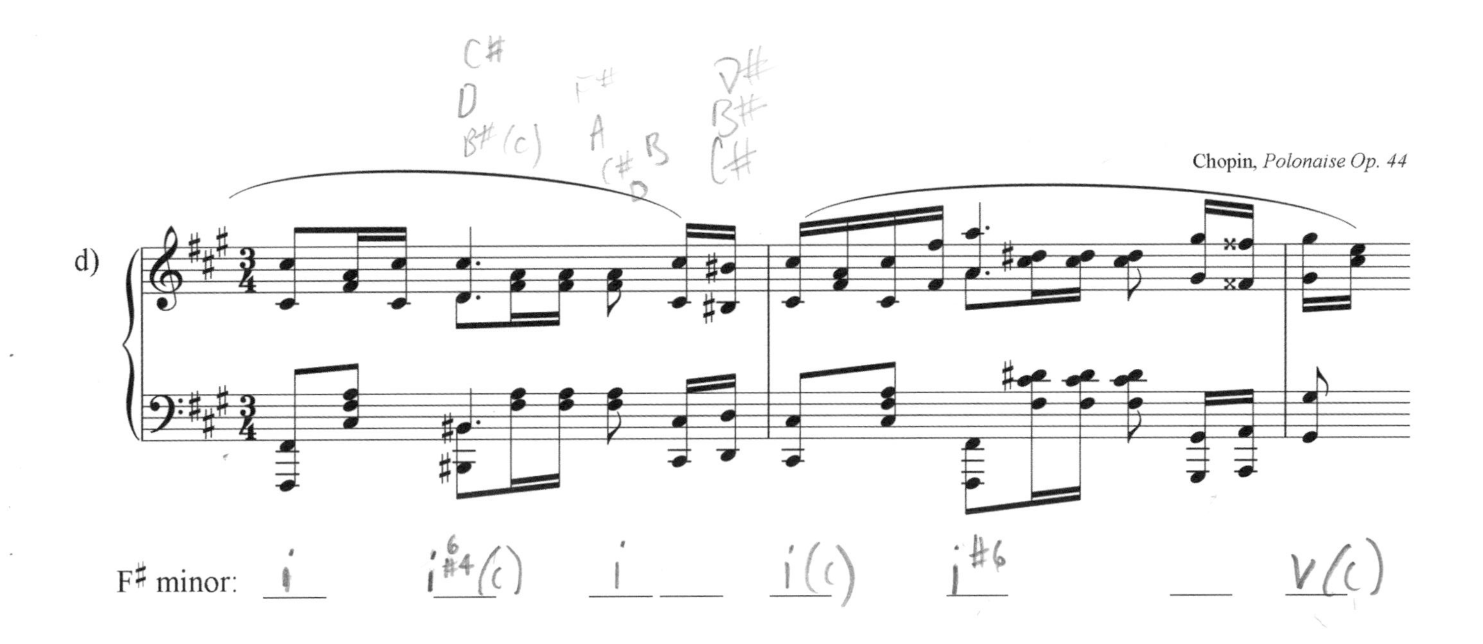

Rossini, *Petite Messe Solennelle, Credo*

E major: ____ ____ ____ ____ ____ ____

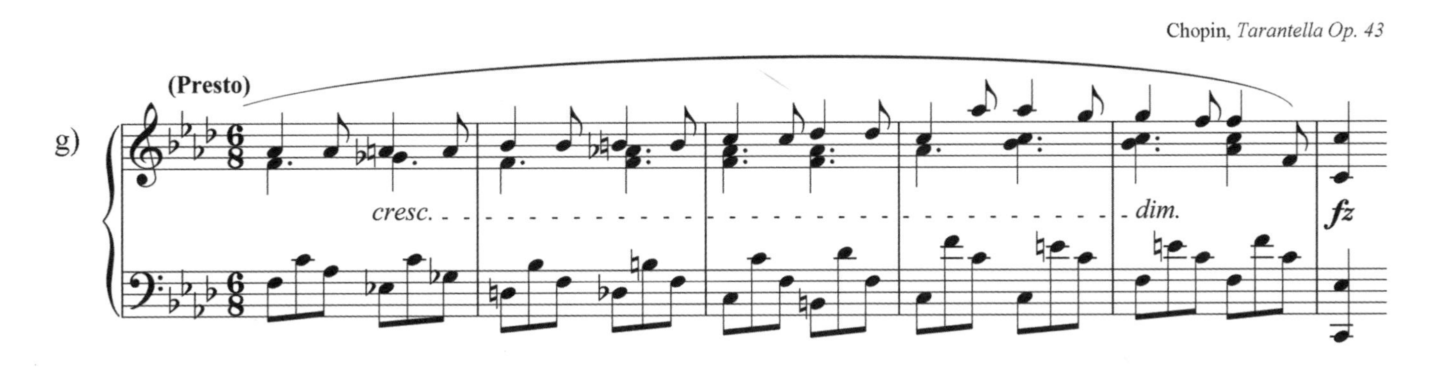

F minor: ____ ____ ____ ____ ____ ____ ____ ____ ____

Schubert, *Die Liebe hat gelogen*

h)

C minor: ____ ____ ____ ____ ____ ____ ____ ____ ____ ____

____ ____ ____ ____ ____ ____ ____ ____ ____ ____ ____ ____

Liszt, *Sonnetto del Petracca 104*

i)

E major: ____ ____ ____ ____ ____

____ ____ ____ ____ ____

7. Study the *Valse Allemande from Carnaval, Op. 9* by Schumann on the next page, then answer the questions below:

a) Mark the length of the pedal note which occurs at 2 places in the score with a └──────┘

b) Identify the chords marked 1 - 10. You may use words or any acceptable method of notation. Show clearly the inversion used and whether each chord is major, minor, diminished or augmented. The prevailing key must be indicated.

A♭ D F

1. ____________________

2. ____________________ Key: __________

3. ____________________ Key: __________

4. ____________________ Key: __________

5. ____________________

6. ____________________

7. ____________________

8. ____________________ Key: __________

9. ____________________

10. ____________________

con ped.
pp
con ped.
sf
f
p
ritard.
ff

8. Study the extract from Mendelssohn's Songs Without Words, then mark in the score, using capital letters for identification, the following:

A a half bar that consists notes of the dominant thirteenth chord in 1st inversion. Bar _____

B a flattened leading note chord in 1st inversion in a major key. Bar _____

C a chromatic supertonic 7th discord in C major. Bar _____

D a Neapolitan chord that is preceded by an appoggiatura in the right hand. Bar _____

E a secondary dominant 7th chord in G major. Bar _____

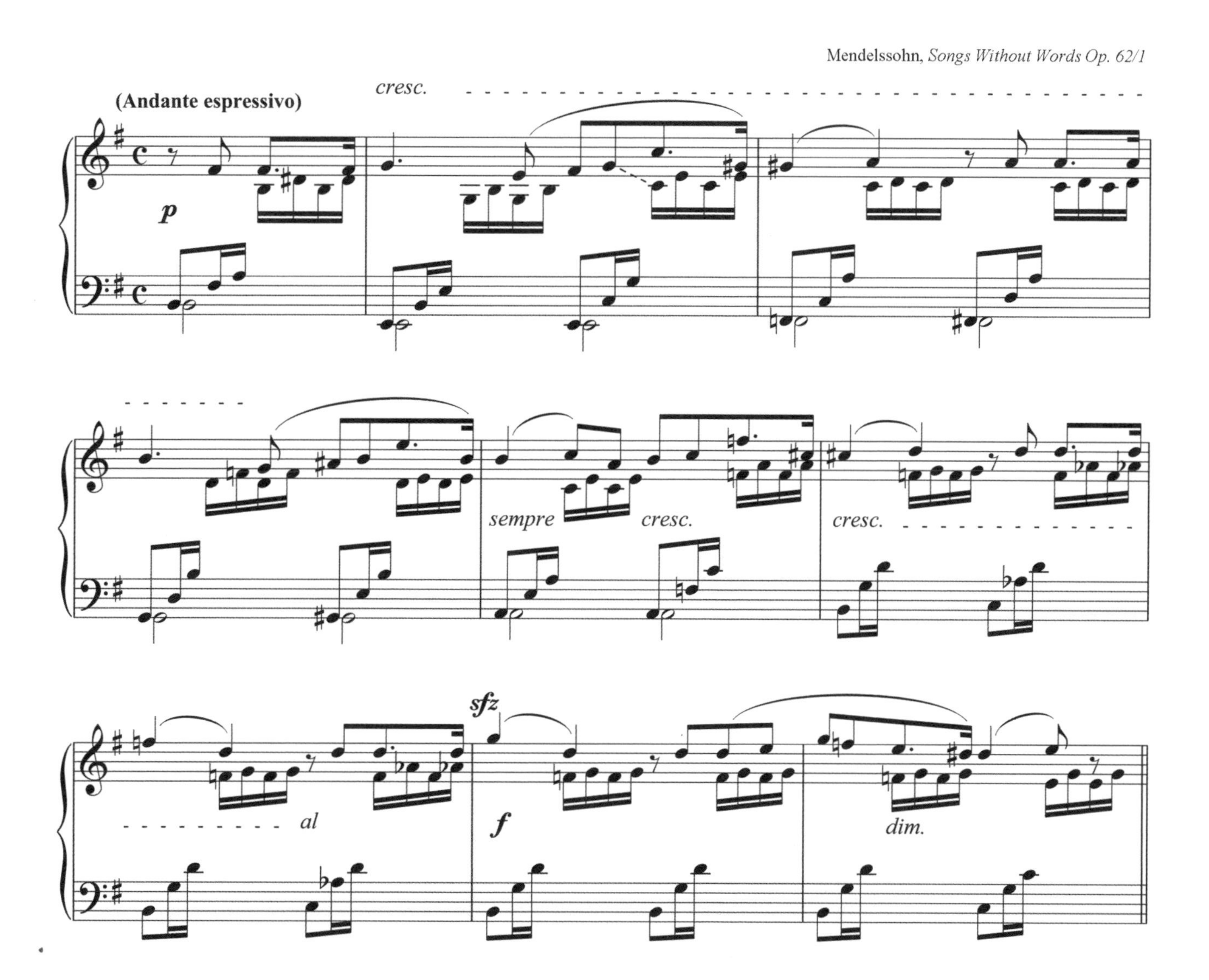

Section II

The Trio Sonata Textures

Essentials of Three-Part Writing

The most common instrumental combination in the middle and late baroque period was the trio sonata: two melodic instruments supported by the basso continuo. Figured bass is often provided for the keyboardist, who nevertheless, often doubles the notes already present in the melodic parts. Passing notes, suspensions and other melodic decorations form the essential movement found in most trio sonatas. Outstanding masters of the trio sonata include Corelli, Vivaldi, Purcell and J.S. Bach.

As students are required to complete trio sonatas in the Grade 8 examination, it is important for now to observe some principles of three-part writing.

Melodic Movement

With the increased harmonic implications in a 3-part texture, it is important to maintain sufficient melodic and rhythmic movement to generate the sense of musical direction.

(i) Use **arpeggiation** and **chordal skips** cautiously, in keeping with the style.

Corelli, *Corrente Op. 1 No. 10*

(ii) **The non-harmony notes** – passing notes, accented passing notes, auxiliary notes, suspensions and appoggiaturas, are most useful in providing melodic movement that would weaken the harmonic implications.

Purcell

(iii) The **tie** and **syncopation** are invaluable in providing melodic independence, both as harmony notes and as suspensions.

It is not recommended that the 2 melodic parts be tied at the same time, but it is possible if the bass part maintains rhythmic continuity.

(iv) **Repeated notes** should be avoided, but used when they occur as a characteristic feature of the thematic figure.

(v) **Pedal point** – Most commonly found in the bass, melodic movement in the other parts have to be sustained over a pedal point.

Rhythmic Movement

Rhythmic activity needs to be equally divided between the two upper parts for balance. The normal pulse must be kept and well-defined when using ties and syncopations. Most commonly the instrumental parts have:

(i) **Similar rhythmic movement** – This should not be continued for more than a few beats between the two solo instruments. It is common for both parts to move in parallel 3rds or 6ths or in contrary motion.

(ii) **Long notes**

– It is possible for long notes to occur in the upper parts as a recurrent feature of the work.

– Rhythmic movement which occurs in two parts may be balanced by long notes in the third part. The resulting texture is thus not too cluttered.

(iii) **Slow and stately passages**

– There are always slow, stately or hymn-like passages which often do not require quaver or semiquaver movement.

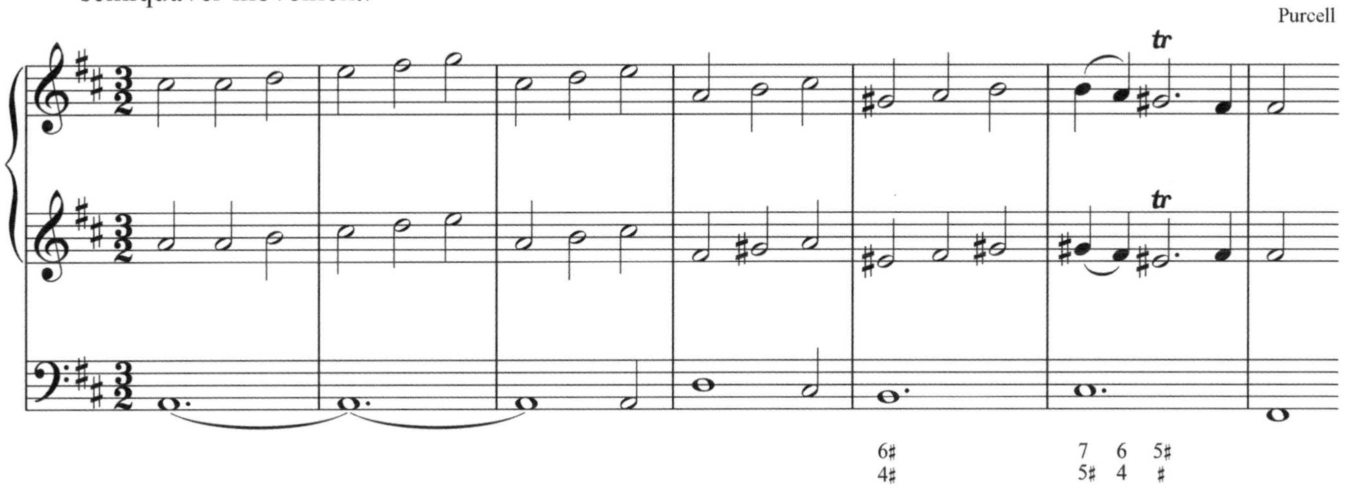

(iv) **Rests**

– Rests are useful and necessary to help ventilate the texture. They also serve to provide a valuable means of obtaining contrast.

– Short rests, such as 𝄾 or 𝄿 can be used to emphasise the entrance of a motivic idea. A rest can also be used to mark the end of a phrase.

– Long and monotonous notes are generally to be avoided as they do not reflect the technique of part writing.

– Imitative writing, however, usually occurs after a rest or rests.

Imitative Writing

Imitation is a type of melodic occurrence which involves at least two parts. The second part *imitates* what the first has previously stated, thus keeping closely to the rhythmic and melodic patterns. It is a compositional device used predominantly in polyphonic works like the canon and fugue.

An imitation may be exact or not exact. It may sound the same melodic intervals as the original or may be slightly modified.

Musical Examples

1. ***Exact imitation*** at the unison occurs here between Violins I and II and at two octaves below in the continuo part. The melodic intervals of the recurrences are the same as in the original.

2. ***Exact imitations*** at intervals other than the unison or octave are achieved by the use of accidentals*.

3. ***Free imitation*** occurs when the size or quality of one or more melodic interval is different from the corresponding intervals in the original occurrence.

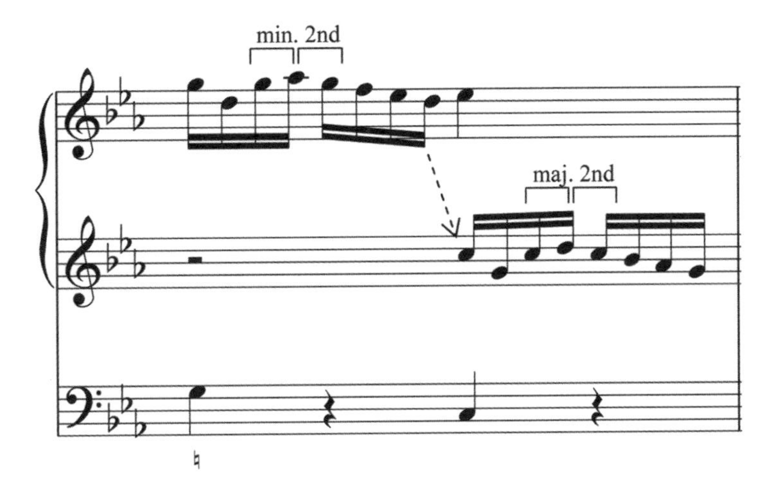

4. The essential point of any imitation is rhythmic, rather than melodic. The size of an interval (e.g. 2nd, 3rd or 4th) may be changed in an imitation. An imitation may involve the manipulation of a fragment of the original idea or used in combination with other devices, such as the sequence and repetition.

The passage above shows ***canonic*** writing, where the use of imitation is significantly continuous, lasting beyond the length of the original motive. Instead of a definite ending, imitative passages often dissolve into further development.

9. Complete the following trio sonata passages using imitation, bearing in mind the principles of voice-leading, maintenance of rhythmic interest, melodic independence and harmonic coherence. The imitations used need not be exact, but it is always desirable to retain the melodic shape.

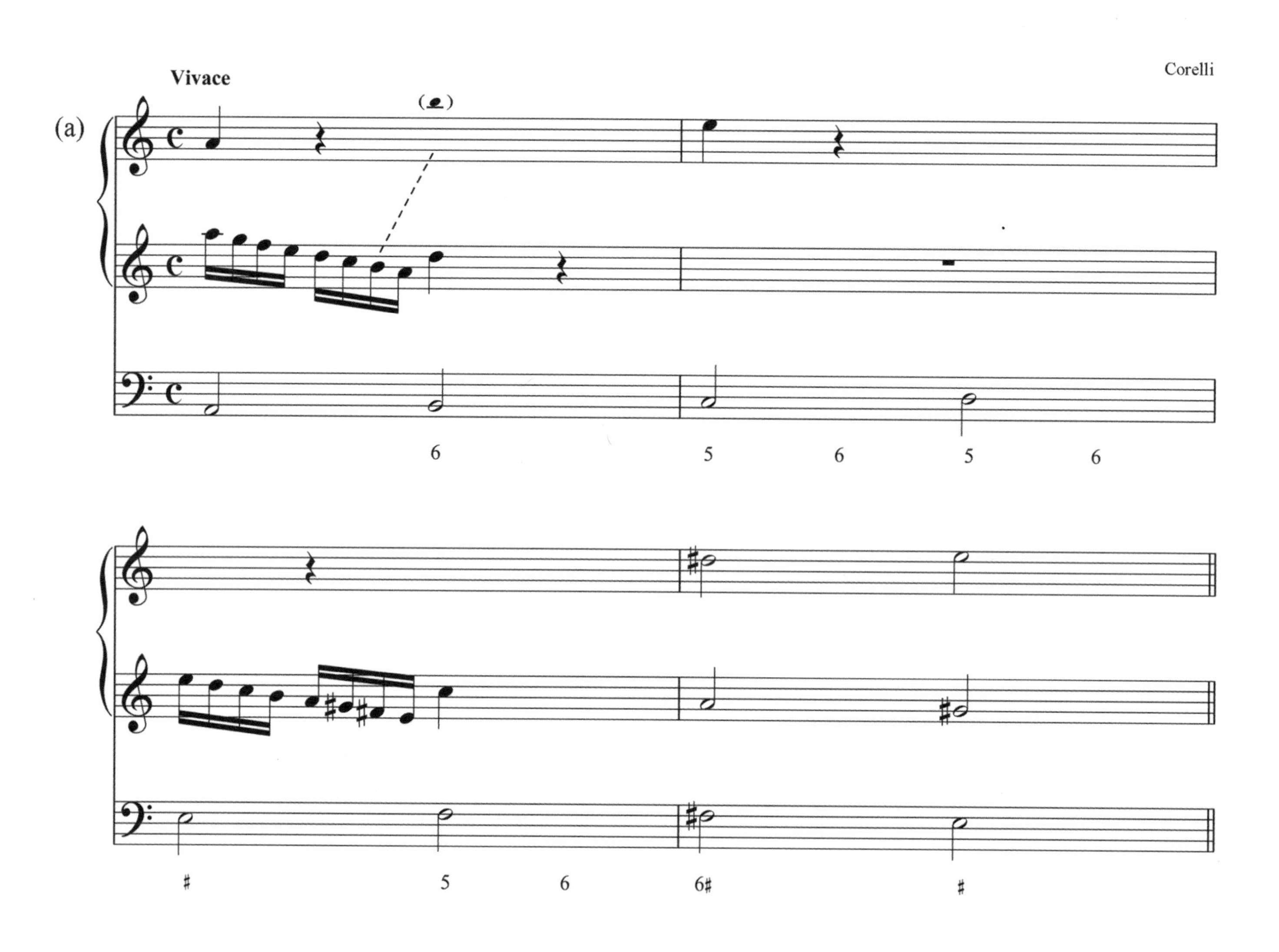

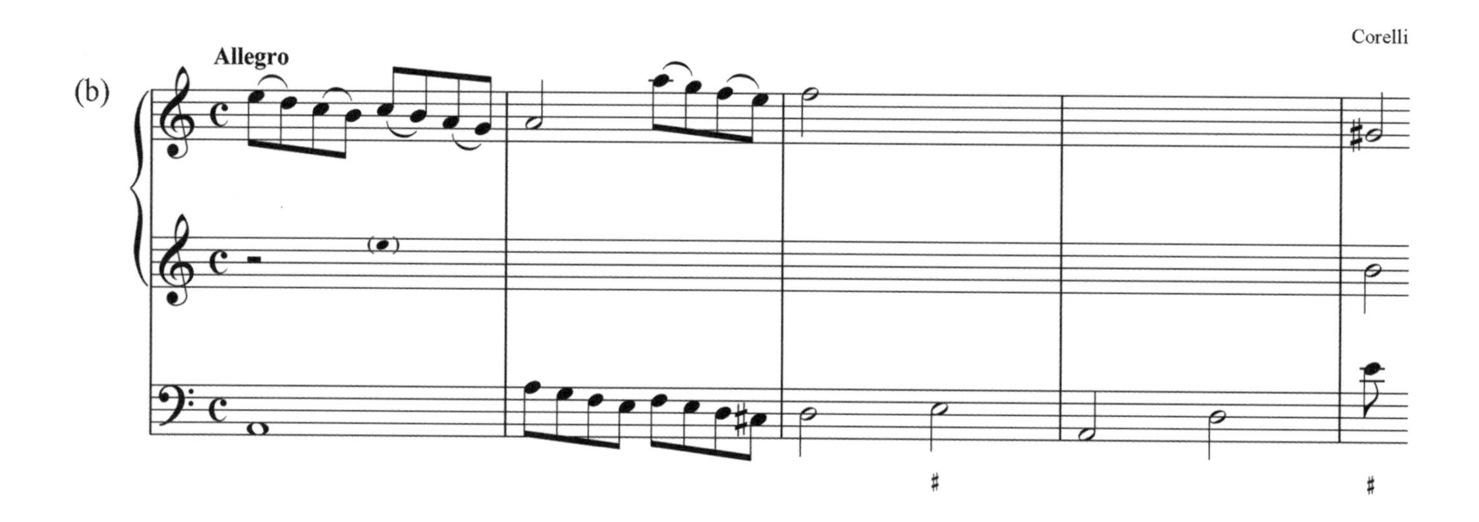

(c)
Allegro
Corelli
(d)
Allegro moderato
Purcell
(e)
Allegro
Handel

The Trio Sonatas

This topic continues to develop further understanding of the trio sonata features. There are two useful types of exercises – first to analyse and study selected trio sonatas and next to complete the upper instrumental parts of the given works. Besides notating keys and chords in the analysis exercises, stylistic features of these works are to be observed. The student should study how musical ideas are spun out from the opening motives and how rhythmic consistency and variety are achieved.

What compositional and musical features can you recognise in the trio sonata below?

(i) This is a gigue in $\frac{12}{8}$ time with the skipping rhythm ♩♪ maintained throughout except at the cadences in bars 3, 4, 6 and 9 (notice the use of long notes).

(ii) Notice the use of many chordal skips, including octave leaps.

(iii) Where quaver movement is generated simultaneously in the two violin parts, consonant harmonic intervals exist predominantly.

(iv) In bar 5, part-writing is evident with the higher notes of Violin I forming an independent line.

(v) Non-harmony notes such as passing notes, suspensions and changing notes help to provide rhythmic and melodic vitality to the music.

10. Study the following trio sonata extracts. Analyse the harmony, keys, modulations and suspensions used. Also observed the stylistic practices and treatment of rhythm, imitation and use of non-harmony notes.

[Write keys and chords]

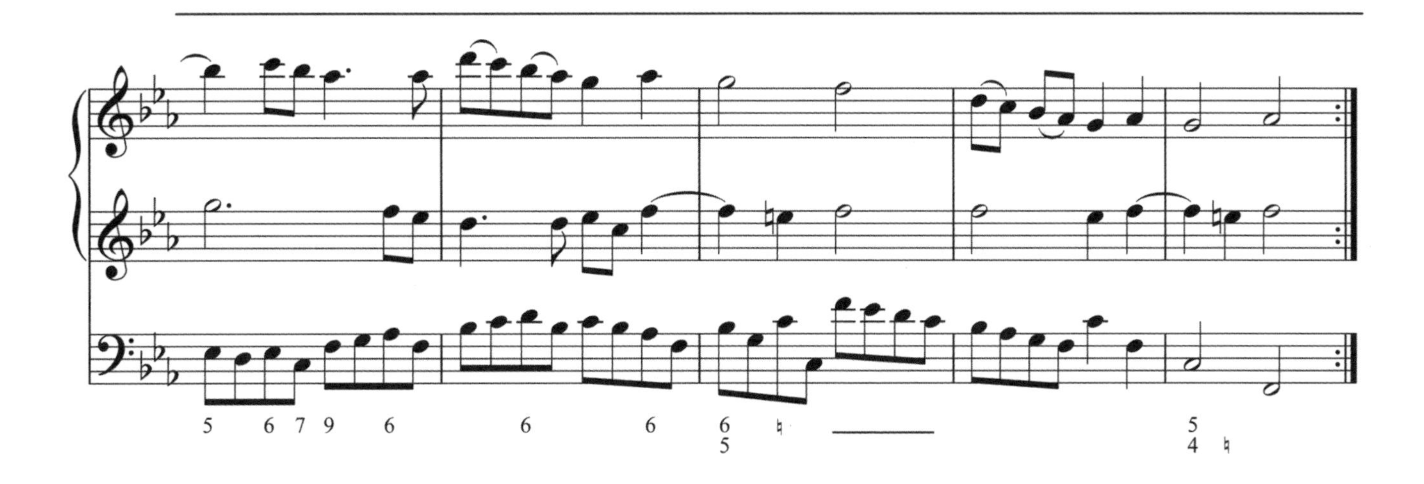

(b)

Affettuoso

Telemann: Sonata in A minor

[Write keys and chords]

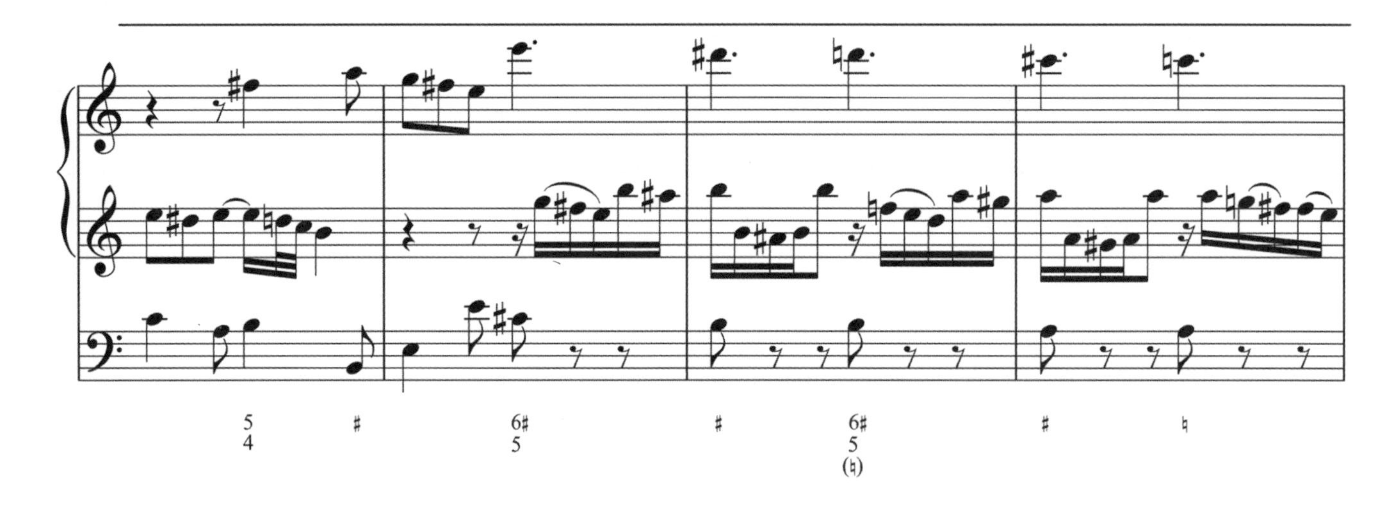

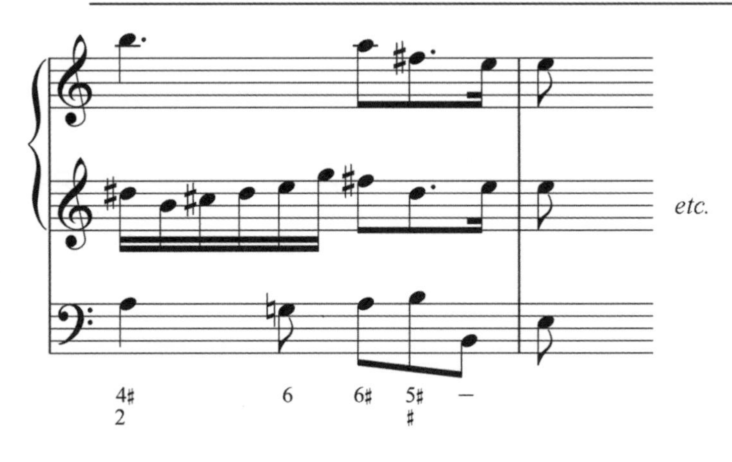

etc.

[Write keys and chords]

[Write keys and chords]

11. Complete the two upper parts of each of the trio sonata passages below by following the figuring shown under the basso continuo.

Corelli

Telemann
Allegro
(c)

Allegro ma non troppo

Jean-Marie Leclair, *Sonata in D minor Op. 4 No. 1*

(d)

Allegro
Corelli, *Corente, Sonata No. 1 Op. 2*
(e)

Boyce

Adagio
Cervetto
(Adapted)
(g)

J.S. Bach
Largo
(h)

Section III

Pianoforte Writing

Writing For Piano

Writing in the keyboard (piano) style requires a sound knowledge of harmonic and melodic movement. While chords need to progress according to rules of voice-leading, there is a need to develop stylistic awareness and an understanding of keyboard textures. At Grade 8, the student will be required to complete a short passage for keyboard based on musical styles practiced by composers from the time of Haydn onwards. Musical ideas, motives and rhythms from the given openings often provide clues that would lead to the answers. Exact reproductions of the composers' versions though, are not expected. Any working which is musically, harmonically and stylistically convincing will be accepted.

Some practical experience at the keyboard is necessary. Piano students may nevertheless find their exposure to repertory and practical skills an advantage. However, before commencing on the exercises, it is deemed worthy for all students to observe some keyboard writing techniques, rules and compositional styles.

Pianoforte Writing Techniques

(i) Directional stems
These must be clearly presented.

(a) Notes that are to be played together share one common stem.

(b) Up and down stems are used to show the movement of parts in a multi-tier texture.

(c) Notes with different rhythms, held notes etc. also need independent directional stems.

(ii) Doubling

Either the right hand or the left hand may be doubled in octaves.

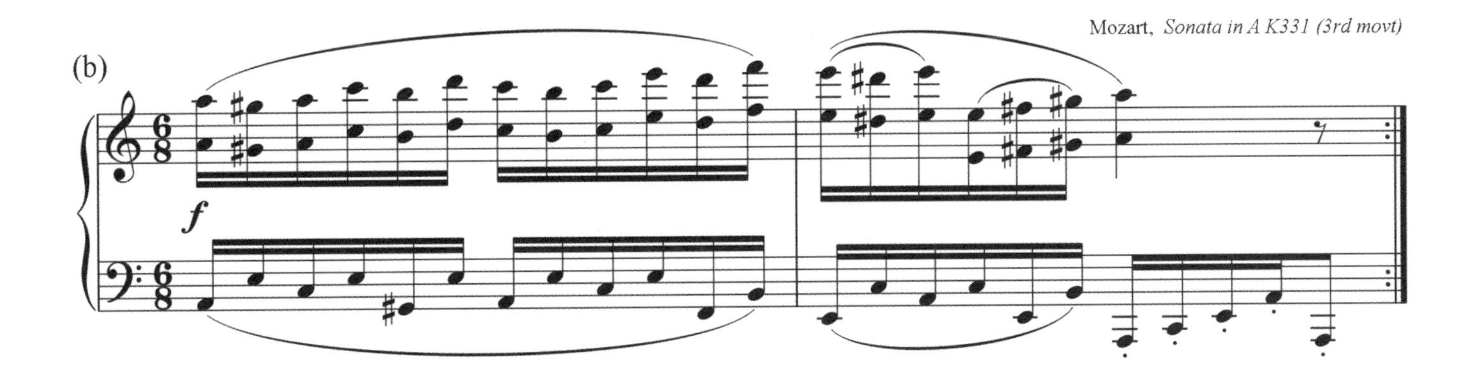

(c) The 3rd of a major chord, leading note or chromatic dissonant note may be doubled, provided there are other notes in the chord which are doubled to balance the effect.

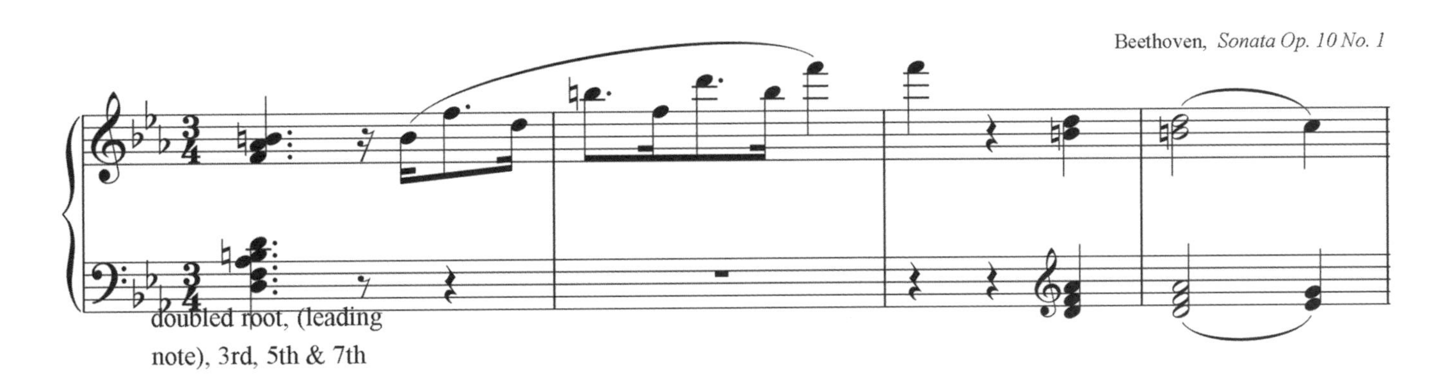

(iii) Consecutive 5ths and 8ves

(a) These should not occur between an upper part and a bass part. It is however accepted in a unison melodic passage.

(b) Consecutive 5ths in the right-hand part are not allowed, though acceptable in the left-hand accompaniment figures.

(iv) Spacing

As a working rule, notes in the lower register, between and should be more than a 3rd apart. For notes below more than an octave apart is preferred.

(v) Hand Position

(a) Care should be taken not to write combinations of notes which the hands cannot play. Always try to imagine the feel of the keyboard under the fingers. Awkward hand movements should be avoided.

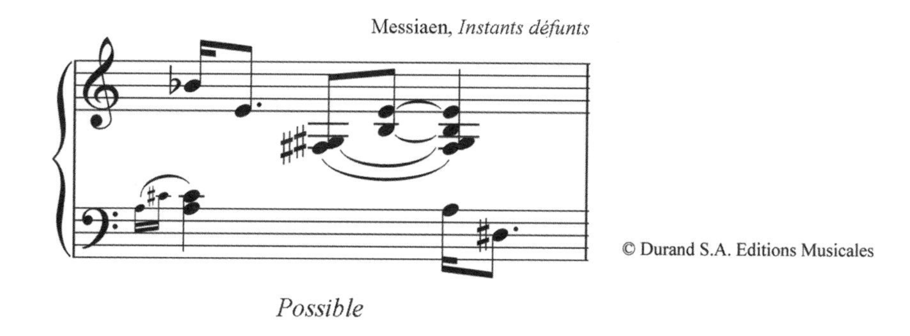

Possible

(b) The stretch of a 10th or more into an arpeggio is possible. Make sure that the notes are playable.

(vi) Texture

The texture in a piano passage may vary from a mixture of two or three notes to six or more notes depending on factors such as the style, character and tempo.

Commonly Used Piano Accompaniment Styles and Textures

There are different ways of using harmony and rhythm for keyboard writing. Rules of voice-leading still apply and should be observed accordingly.

(i) Block chord / harmonic style

Beethoven, *Sonata Op. 53 (1st movt)*

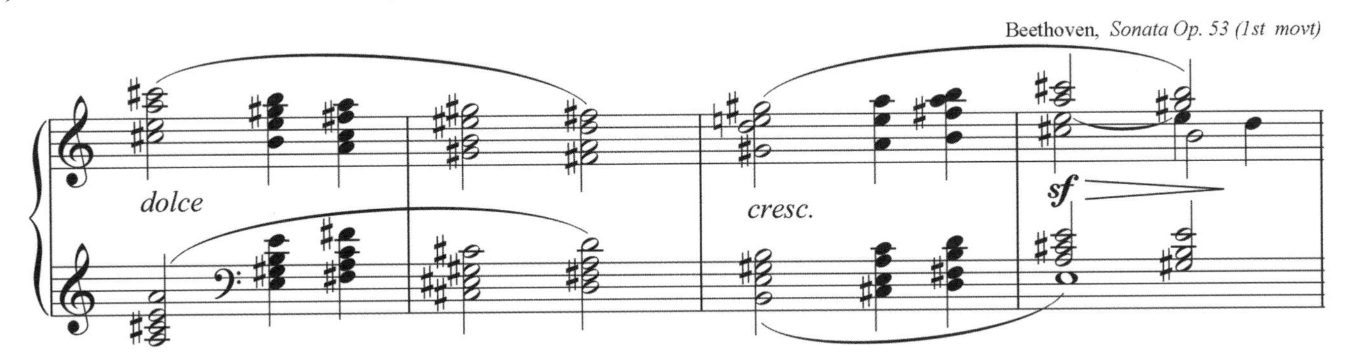

(ii) Leaping bass accompaniment

Usually the bass note of a chord is sounded on the first beat of a bar followed by the complete chord. The sustaining pedal is often used to prolong the effect of the bass. This style is popular in dance-like music such as the waltz, mazurka and ländler.

Tchaikovsky, *Waltz Op.39*

(iii) Alberti bass accompaniment

This is a broken chord figure with its repetitive pattern often found in the bass part.

Mozart, *Sonata in A minor K310 (1st movt)*

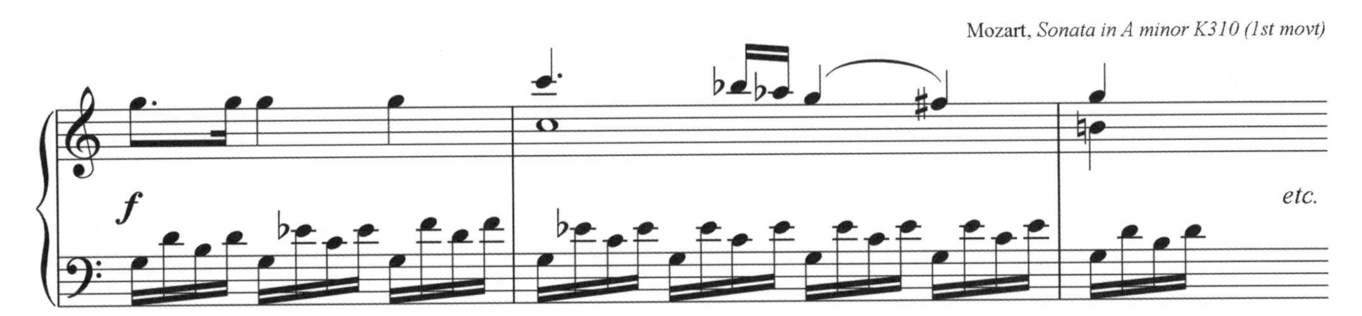

(iv) Broken chords and arpeggios

A great deal of piano accompaniment writing involves the use of **broken chords** and **arpeggios**. Often, these figures can be regarded as vertical chords with notes played one after another. Consecutive 5ths and 8ves must be avoided and dissonances must be resolved accordingly.

The passage above may thus be reduced harmonically to:

Having discussed pianoforte textures, the student will now proceed to the study of stylistic features found in the various practice periods. The Grade 8 ABRSM syllabus requires the student to complete a given passage of piano music which dates from the classical era. In the following three topics, the student will be presented with the synopses of the most important stylistic elements from selected works for purpose of study and analysis.

Stylistic Study: Classical Works

The Classical Style (1730 - 1820)

This period which spans approximately a decade, brings forth a collection of piano literature which is simple and serene, with perfect balance of form and content. The fortepiano replaces the harpsichord as the most desired keyboard instrument. The sonata form was established during this period, used predominantly by the leading composers of the era – Dussek, Clementi, Haydn, Mozart and Beethoven.

Melody

Classical melodies are characteristically written in well-articulated and distinct phrases, usually two or four bars in length. Most melodies are constructed on simple chord figuration, decorated by passing notes, turns and appoggiaturas.

Mozart, *Sonata in B♭, K333 (3rd movt)*

The technique of motivic development was favoured by both Haydn and Beethoven. The use of sequences and repetitions was a phenomenon of classical works. Play the following passage from Haydn's Sonata in C major XVI/50.

Play the example below from Beethoven's Pathetique Sonata Op. 13.

From these examples, we can identify the stylistic features that dominate classical works:

Harmony

The harmonic rhythm is usually simple, straightforward, coinciding with the strong accents made pronounced by the barlines. Apart from the diatonic chords, secondary dominants and diminished 7th, the Neapolitan 6th and augmented 6th chords are also employed, justified by the resolutions of the dissonances, established cadences and key structures.

Rhythm

The rhythmic patterns are usually consistent. With the development of thematic and motivic materials, the accents and predictable rhythms give beauty to the music, thus providing the pulse and the momentum that drive the mood and spirit of the works.

Texture

Mostly homophonic in texture, the melodies are usually accompanied by accompaniment patterns such as broken chords or alberti bass. The texture is never too cluttered, thick or complex.

Form

The inclination towards symmetry in phrasing and form leads to periodic sentences and formalized sections being organised around related key structures. Most works are written in the extended binary, ternary, variation, rondo or sonata forms.

Though not all classical works necessarily conform to the features mentioned above, nevertheless the student may find the key points helpful in developing their musical perception of the classical period.

12. Study the opening section of this Rondo by Haydn, then complete the passage that follows.

13. Complete the missing harmonies in the passage below.

14. Complete the opening section of the 4th Variation by Beethoven from *13 Variations in A Major*.

15. Complete the Adagio section given below from Mozart's *Fantasia in D minor, K397*.

16. Complete the opening section of Beethoven's first piano sonata. Most students who have played this work in their solo piano study may find this exercise very enlightening.

Stylistic Study: Romantic Works

The Romantic Style (1810 - 1920)

Of all the musical styles and periods, the bulk of piano repertory and study materials are written in the 19th century. In contrast to the universality, serenity and restraint of the classical style, the aesthetic ideals of romanticism extol the artistic freedom of the individual and the unrestrained expression of personal feelings[1]. Romantic art cherishes freedom, movement and passion, as against the classical ideals of order, control and equilibrium. It is haunted by a spirit of longing and emotional tension. Thus the best expressions of personal feelings are found in works written for the individual – the solo voice and the piano.

The Piano of the 19th century was quite different from the one used during Mozart's time. It was reshaped, enlarged and mechanically improved; capable of producing a full, firm tone at any required dynamic level and responding in every way to demands for expressiveness and virtuosity.

As **technical demands** became more exacting, new styles of piano music emerged. The form, intensity and quality of expression defer widely, from the classically oriented Schubert and Mendelssohn, to the strongly innovative expression of Schumann, Chopin, Liszt and Brahms. Late romantic works also reflect ethnic influence and impressionistic tendencies including those of Grieg, Faure, Albeniz and Rachmaninoff.

The romantic ideals, sonorities and compositional techniques for the piano led to several works with **small musical structures**, mostly lyric character pieces: *nocturnes, impromptus, songs without words, intermezzi, musical moments* etc. Nearly all works are suggestive of some specific mood or scene, sometimes specified in the title. Major piano works were also written during the period which include *concertos, variations, fantasias, sonatas, ballades and scherzi.*

[1] Denes Agay, Teaching Piano (1981)

Melody and Texture

The romantic piano literature is much inclined towards homophonic or multi-tier writing. However, some *contrapuntal* writing may occur, which are often short passages that add harmonic and rhythmic colour to the melodic flow.

Here, the imitation appears momentarily in the inner part, all within clear harmonic structures.

In a *homophonic* texture, it is a characteristic feature for a single melodic line to be supported by chords or accompaniment patterns. The following examples illustrate some of the practices.

(a) A single melodic line in the treble is accompanied by harmonically colourful and varied chords.

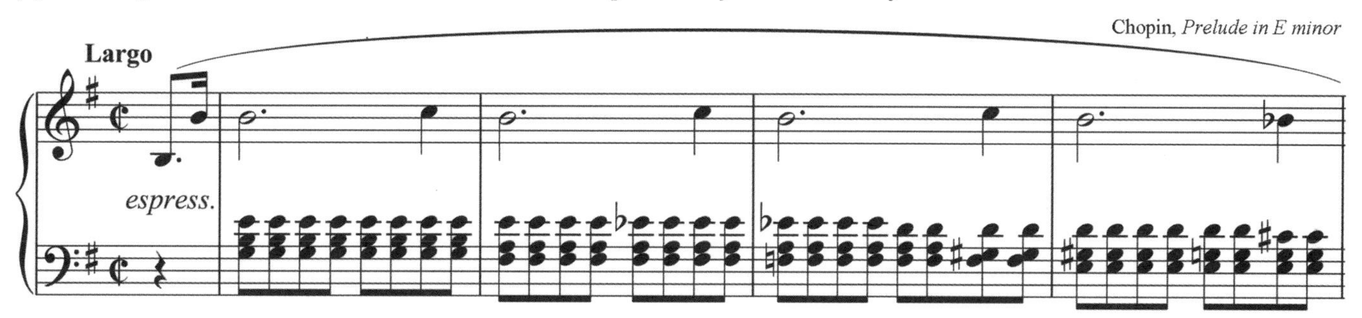

(b) An expressive melody in the bass is accompanied by stable harmonies above.

(c) The melodic line is in the highest part, with the driving triplet figure in the bass, amidst the *chordal homophony*.

A *multi-tier texture* consists of a melody, bass line and inner parts. The melody may appear, in any of the parts, notably identified by directional stems and often with a contrasting rhythm to the subordinate parts.

In the example below, the melody is in the inner part, with a distinct supporting bass and flowing broken chords above. Play the extract and bring out the inner part with its sweet singing melody.

Formal Design

Melodic phrases are usually repeated to form larger units, sometimes with modified repetitions. The changes may be minimal, such as the addition of grace notes or may involve more substantial melodic and rhythmic alterations. In the short piano works, variations of the theme usually do not deviate much from the original melodic, harmonic and rhythmic elements notated by the composer. In larger works however, further development can occur with new material evolving, thus expanding on the formal structure and design.

Harmony

The harmony used in the romantic era evolved out of the need for expression: to intensify effects, to create suspense or simply to bring a twist to the harmonic colour. Characteristics of Romantic harmony include delayed resolution of dissonances, the use of complex chords and suspense created in the tonality. Borrowed chords, remote modulations and enharmonic changes may create some sense of uncertainty. However, tonality still exists, despite the deceptive cadences, abrupt modulations and ubiquitous chromatic alterations, all accomplished within the discipline of harmonic voice-leading.

Play and study the *Barcarolle Op. 37 No. 6* by Tchaikovsky, paying special attention to the compositional features.

17. Study the two musical extracts that follow. Mark out the phrases and analyse the harmonies based on the given keys and modulations. Observe the use of materials, texture, climatic points etc. Then play through the passages slowly and listen to the effects created.

(a)

(b)

18. Complete the following extracts taken from the Romantic repertory by keeping close to the ideas presented. You are not required to reproduce a version similar to the original works. Any logically harmonised and creative musical presentations are strongly encouraged and acceptable.

(b)
Tchaikovsky
Allegro non troppo
la melodie con molto espressione
p
mf
p
p

(c)

Chopin, *Prelude in A*

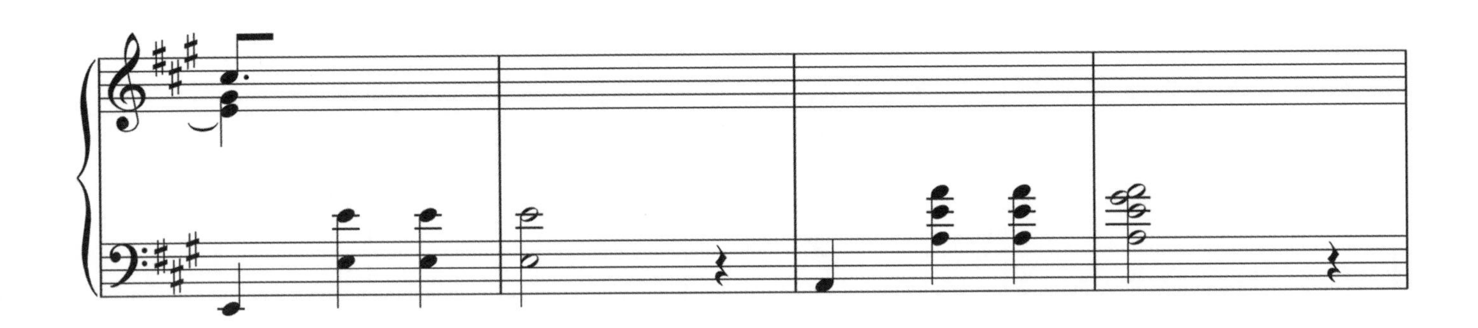

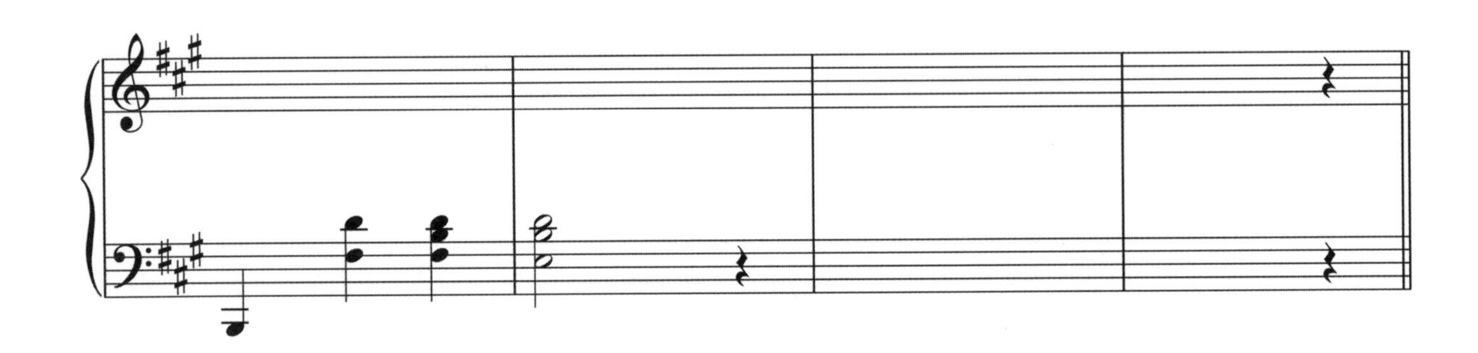

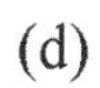

Grieg, *Little Children Op. 66 No. 17*

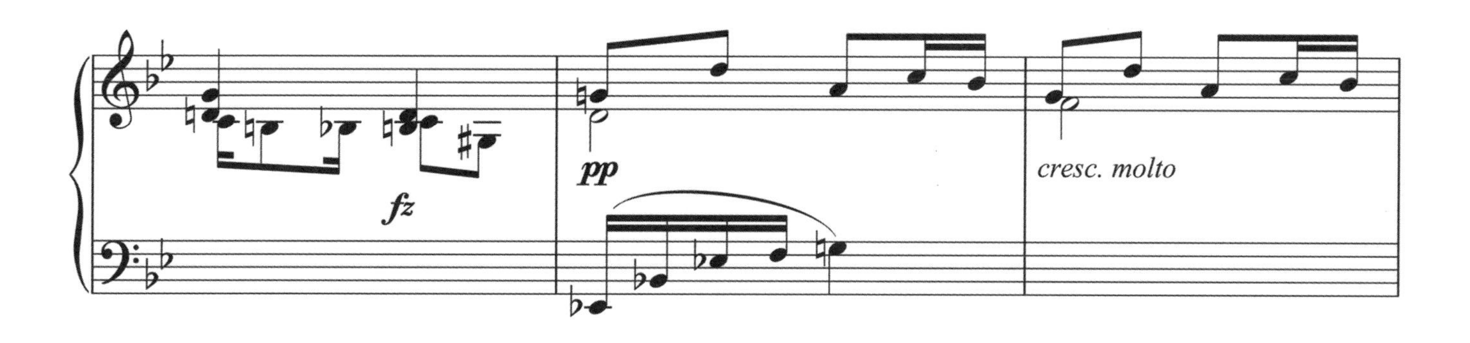

Stylistic Study: Modern Works

20th Century Works – An Introduction

The music of the 20th century reflects profound changes that affect the history and development of western music. It is a period of search, a time of turmoil, experimentation and discovery. Unlike the earlier eras, it does not possess the unanimous styles and ideals exhibited in the forms of musical expression. Instead it shows such diversity in compositional styles and trends, notably *post-modernism, impressionism, neoclassicism, serialism and individualism.* Combinations and variations of these styles often occur, intermingled with jazz and folk idioms. With a good understanding of the history of 20th century music and adequate knowledge of the piano repertory of the period, students would be able to develop greater interest, awareness and appreciation of such musical works. Nevertheless, this topic attempts to identify some of the composition techniques with reference to the musical elements – rhythm, melody, tonality, harmony, texture and form. A recommended reading list and reference have been included on page 117 of this workbook.

Rhythm

Perhaps the greatest innovations in 20th century music lie in the domain of rhythm – freedom from the regular metric pulse. The Russian and East European composers including Bartok, Prokofiev, Stravinsky, Kodaly, Kabalevsky and Khachaturian often introduce and integrate speech accents into their rhythmic framework. *Syncopations* and *shifted accents* give rise to more complex rhythmic patterns that in turn create a sense of urgency and intense excitement.

a) *Syncopation*

Bartok, *Mikrokosmos Vol. 5 No. 22*

Molto vivace, ♩ = 160

f strepitoso

b) *Shifted Accents* in the left hand part

Prokofiev, *Vision Fugitives Op. 22 No. 5*

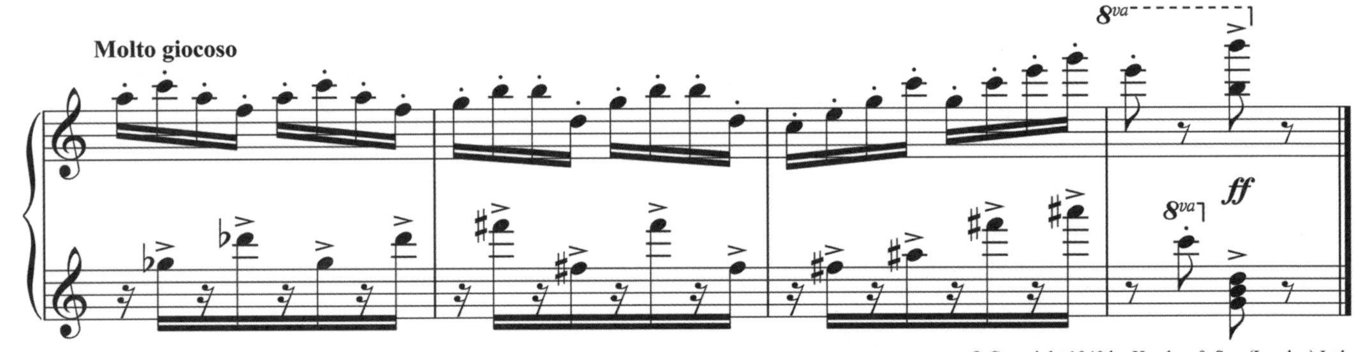

c) *Multimetric writing* becomes common, of which meters change frequently. Intricate combinations such as $\frac{5}{8} = \frac{2}{8} + \frac{3}{8}$ or $\frac{7}{8} = \frac{2}{8} + \frac{2}{8} + \frac{3}{8} = \frac{4}{8} + \frac{3}{8}$ create rhythmic effects that break away from the "tyranny of the barline".

Melody

As music may be written in free rhythm of prose or even improvisatory style, melodic lines of the 20th century are often less vocally inspired. They often do not grow from established harmonic framework. Instead, repetitions of pitches or variations of a single motivic cell serve to unfold discursive or fragmented melodies. In the example below, one hears the same notes in different situations, altered primarily by the subtle rhythmic implications* .

Harmony

With the evolution of modal melodies, unrestricted use of dissonances and chromaticisms, new ideas of harmony emerged. These include the free use of triadic harmonies, non-functional chords, polychords, note clusters, quartal harmony and other diatonic configurations formed from new concepts of scales.

Observe the use of unresolved (non-functional) 7th chords below.

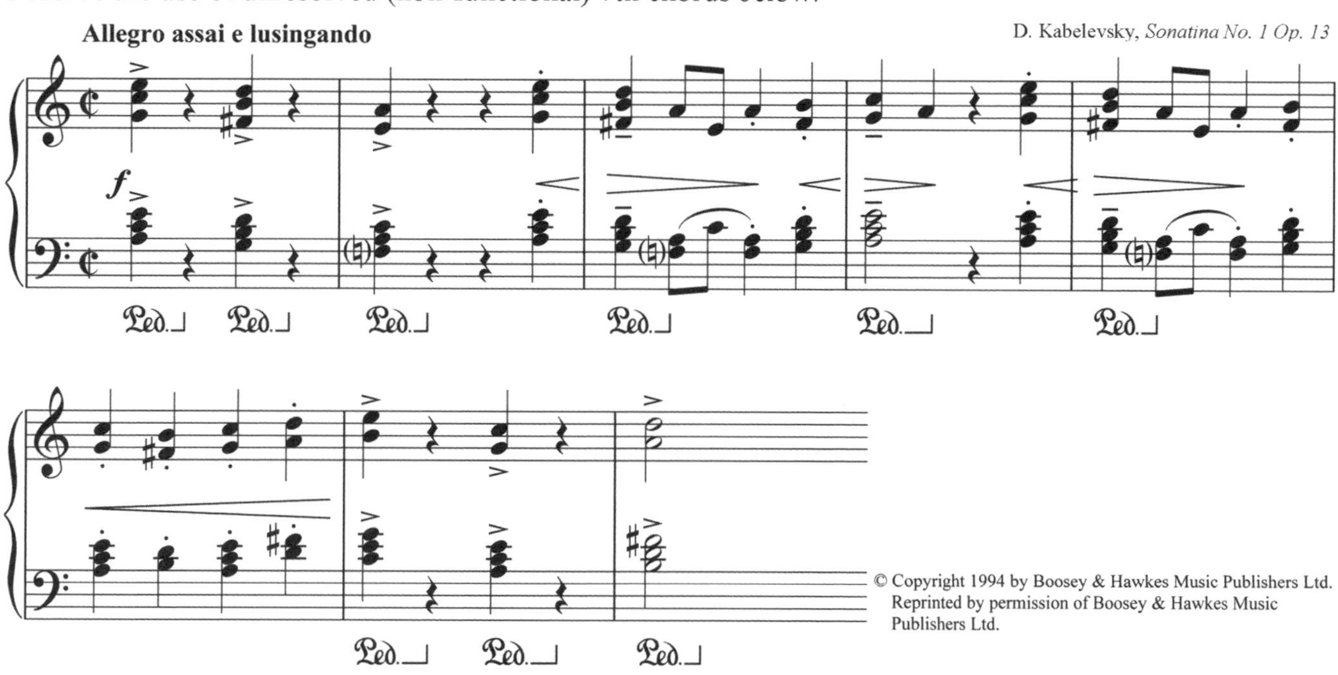

Tonality

Many modern compositions lack the sense of tonality found in traditional works. Instead, repetitions of a particular note may form the key centre supporting a work. Alternatively, composers use modes, pentatonic scales, whole-tone scales and other artificial scales in their construction. The example below illustrates how an entire piece is composed based on a chosen series of notes.

The melody takes on a very narrow range, simply based on the given series of notes. Observe the use of counterpoint between the two parts, irregular phrasing, simple rhythm and accents.

Form

Form and structure in 20th century music can be examined from two points of view: the **outer** form, which refers to the sectional arrangement and the **inner** form, which constitutes the thematic and motivic connections.

In the following example, "Melody Divided" illustrates an overall design which is in free and dissonant harmony. The melodic lines are played alternatively in each hand with dissonant harmonies pitted against them. The last few bars present a "neat" conclusion with a purpose – E minor 7th chord in 1st inversion. Based on the simple principles of repetition and contrast, the materials are combined into an organic whole.

19. Complete the following extracts taken from the 20th century repertory. Study the harmony and rhythmic patterns without confining your ideas to traditional rules and practices. Upon completion of each exercise, play through your working to ensure continuity and coherence.

(a) Complete the missing parts of this variation by Kabalevsky.

(b) Complete the left hand part of this extract.

(c) The piece is entitled, "Grandmother Tells A Ghost Story". Complete the missing piano parts in this extract.

(d) Complete the second section of this March by Paul Hindemith by paying attention to the rhythmic characteristics. The composition was completed in 1931.

(e) Complete the valse entitled "Columbine tanzt" by Bohuslar Martinů.

Section IV

Melodic Composition

Advanced Tonal Melodic Composition

Syllabus Requirements

Melodic composition for the Grade 8 student is based on a given opening for a specified instrument. A thorough understanding of principles in melodic construction is required including key, modulation, harmony, chord progression, form, use of melodic and rhythmic devices.

To acquire a good pass at Grade 8, the student is expected to demonstrate a competent grasp of tonal compositional techniques. The given musical ideas need to be well developed, and reflect the suitability for performance at Grade 8 level by the specified instrumentalist. The melody is expected to be idiomatically conceived, revealing the instrumental range, technical and musical resourcefulness.

Harmonic Vocabulary

A wide range of chords is now available to the student: *the diatonic secondary 7ths, the diminished 7ths, the Neapolitan 6th, the secondary dominants, the augmented 6ths* and other *chromatically altered chords*. This rich harmonic vocabulary is a palette of colours that could be applied to melodies in a diatonic context. Modulations, especially to remote keys can thus be brought about subtly, and more convincingly. Often, melodies based on good harmonic frameworks can be stylistically enhanced by the creative use of rhythm, phrasing, dynamics and articulation.

Modulations

The examination question does not specify any particular modulation or any expected modulatory scheme. Nevertheless, the student is expected to include *at least* one principal modulation. In most cases, a further *two* to *three* temporary key changes are recommended. It is important for the student to be discreet in the choice of keys. A modulation, for example, to the flattened mediant major will not be in keeping with a baroque dance in binary form – a feature more commonly found in late 18th century and 19th century works.

Stylistic Awareness

The student should demonstrate his awareness of styles, not merely in the treatment of keys, but also in the treatment of phraseology, form, rhythmic organization and character of the piece. Stylistic awareness of a Gavotte, for example, is to begin and end each phrase on the half bar. Motivic ideas that contain features such as suspensions, dissonances and syncopations need to be further developed in the course of the composition.

Part-Writing

Part movement is probably the technical skill to be acquired and demonstrated at Grade 8. It is important for the student to note that the underlying harmonic framework will not be defined if there are insufficient harmony notes. On the other hand, too many harmony notes with little rhythmic activity may result in a very triadic and static melody that lacks contour and direction. Thus the use of *part movement* with a strong harmonic scheme is recommended within the single melodic line.

Melodic Writing in the 17th Century

To understand the concept of part movement, study the harmonic structure of the *Sarabande* below and then compare it with its *Double* printed on page 84.

J.S. Bach, *Partita in B minor for Solo Violin*

Sarabande

Some observations:

(i) In this Sarabande, double, triple and even quadruple stops are used to form the harmonies that support the melodic line.

(ii) *Part movement* is much generated in the solo part as the work is intended to be performed unaccompanied. The lower lines and the inner parts thus provide harmonic interest and contrapuntal effect to an otherwise monophonic construction.

(iii) Observe the 2-part counterpoint in bars 3, 14, 15 and 32.

(iv) Several non-harmony notes and chordal skips generate rhythmic interest to the otherwise highly chordal and harmonic texture. Mark in the score, using capital letters for identification, each of the following. Also give the bar number of your answers.

A an appoggiatura (bars 1 to 8) Bar _____

B a suspension in E minor Bar _____

C a lower auxiliary note Bar _____

D an anticipation after bar 22 Bar _____

E an accented passing note in B minor Bar _____

F an imperfect cadence after bar 10 Bar _____

G a diminished 7th chord in E minor Bar _____

H a modulation to A major Bar _____

The whole of the previous *Sarabande* is then varied and treated differently to form a single melodic line with quicker movement of notes in $\frac{9}{8}$ time. The texture, though much lighter, still retains the basic original harmonic scheme.

Double

J.S. Bach, *Partita in B minor for Solo Violin*

Some observations:

(i) The passage contains several wide melodic leaps using chordal notes and octave displacements. By eliminating the non-harmony notes, the harmonic implication becomes clear.

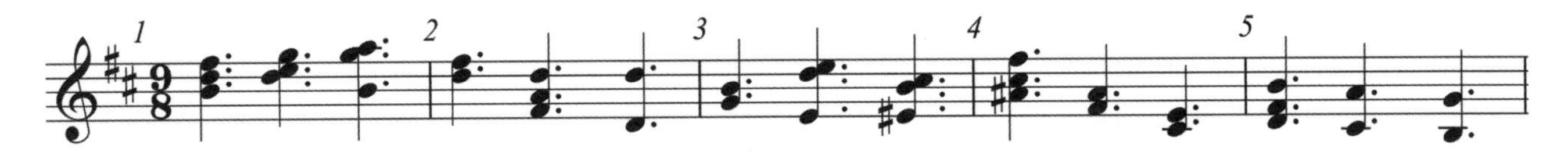

(ii) Wider leaps are used in the 2nd section. Bars 10, 14, 15, 19 and 20 involve melodic intervals of more than an octave. This technique of melodic writing is often recommended for instrumental works which often involve a wide range of notes.

(iii) Once again, can you identify the key changes that occur at the following places?

Bars 12 & 13 ____________________ Bars 18 to 20 ____________________

Bars 14 to 17 ____________________

(iv) Identify the chords marked 1, 2, 3 and 4 in the score, stating the prevailing key.

1. ____________________________________ Key: ____________________

2. ____________________________________ Key: ____________________

3. ____________________________________ Key: ____________________

4. ____________________________________ Key: ____________________

(v) It is important to maintain the single basic affection prevalent in all baroque works – by ensuring that there is constant rhythmic flow and that the materials are spun out from the original motif. Interestingly, *part movement* is often suggested by one or more underlying inner parts.

Can you trace the three melodic parts within this given bar?

20. Compose a melody of not less than 12 bars using each of the following openings for the specified unaccompanied instruments. Continue in the same style and include appropriate performance directions. Write each of your complete melodies on the staves provided.

(a) CELLO

(b) FLUTE

(c) OBOE

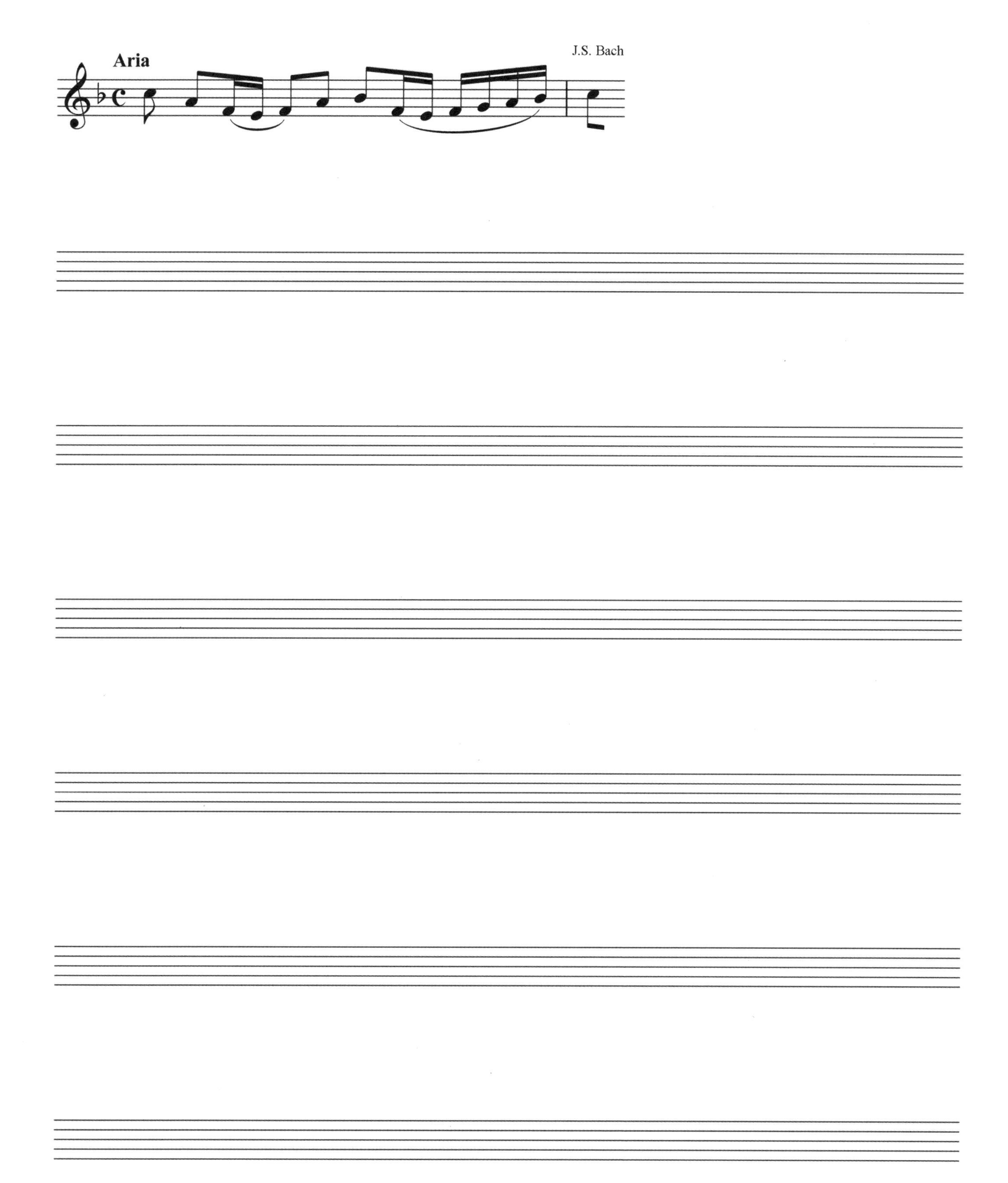

Melodic Writing in the 18th Century

Unlike the Baroque period, most instrumental works of the 18th century are usually accompanied by the piano or the orchestra. Composers were increasingly interested in the interaction between melody and accompaniment and thus have less incentive to write for unaccompanied soloists with contrapuntal part-movement, except perhaps in the form of technical studies. This neglect continued into the Romantic era with melodic writing supported by a more elaborate texture, richer harmonic style and more flexible harmonic rhythm. The inter-dependence of melody and accompaniment is a vital feature of post-baroque tonal melodic writing.

21. Study the musical extracts that follow. Observe the use of harmony, rhythm, melodic ideas, dynamics and expression and then make short notes to reinforce your understanding.

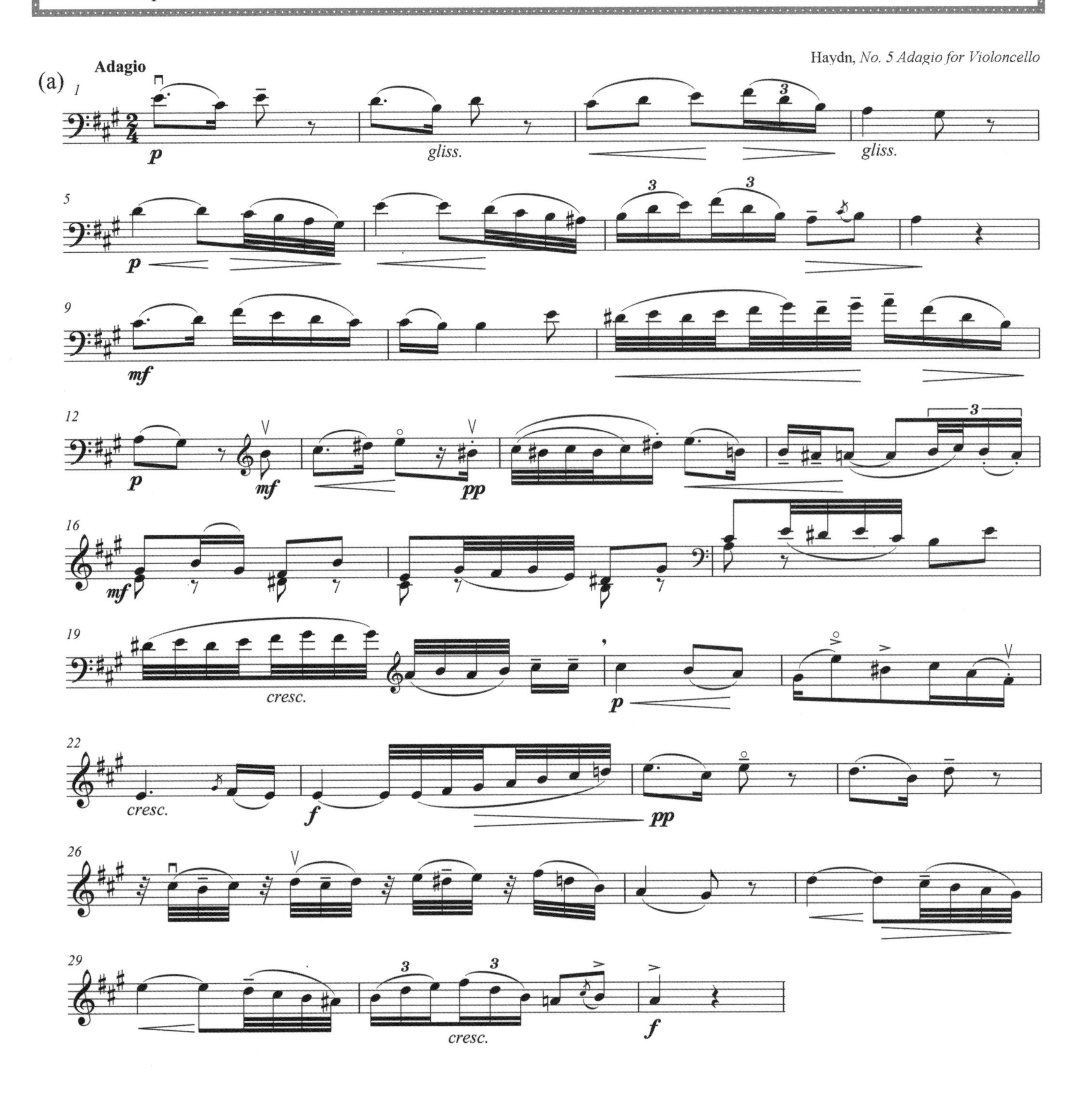

Study Points:

1. The melody is smooth flowing and lyrical, with little part-writing. Double stops are used in bars 16 to 18.

2. A wide range of notes is used with the need to alternate between the treble and bass clefs. Notice that the melodic writing is idiomatic, composed with the specific qualities and characteristics of the cello.

3. Study the phrase structure and motives of the opening bars. Observe how Haydn developed the materials. Make notes on your analysis with the help of the questions below.

(i) Notice the triplet rhythm used in bar 3, where else does it occur in the extract?

____

____

____

(ii) Compare bars 24-31 with bars 1-8. Identify the similarities and differences.

____

____

____

(iii) How does Haydn create melodic interest with only one principal modulation? What keys do you think have been implied? Indicate the bar numbers.

____

____

____

(iv) A variety of rhythms are combined to provide contrast, flow and musical direction. Discuss how these elements bring coherence to the work.

____

____

____

(b)

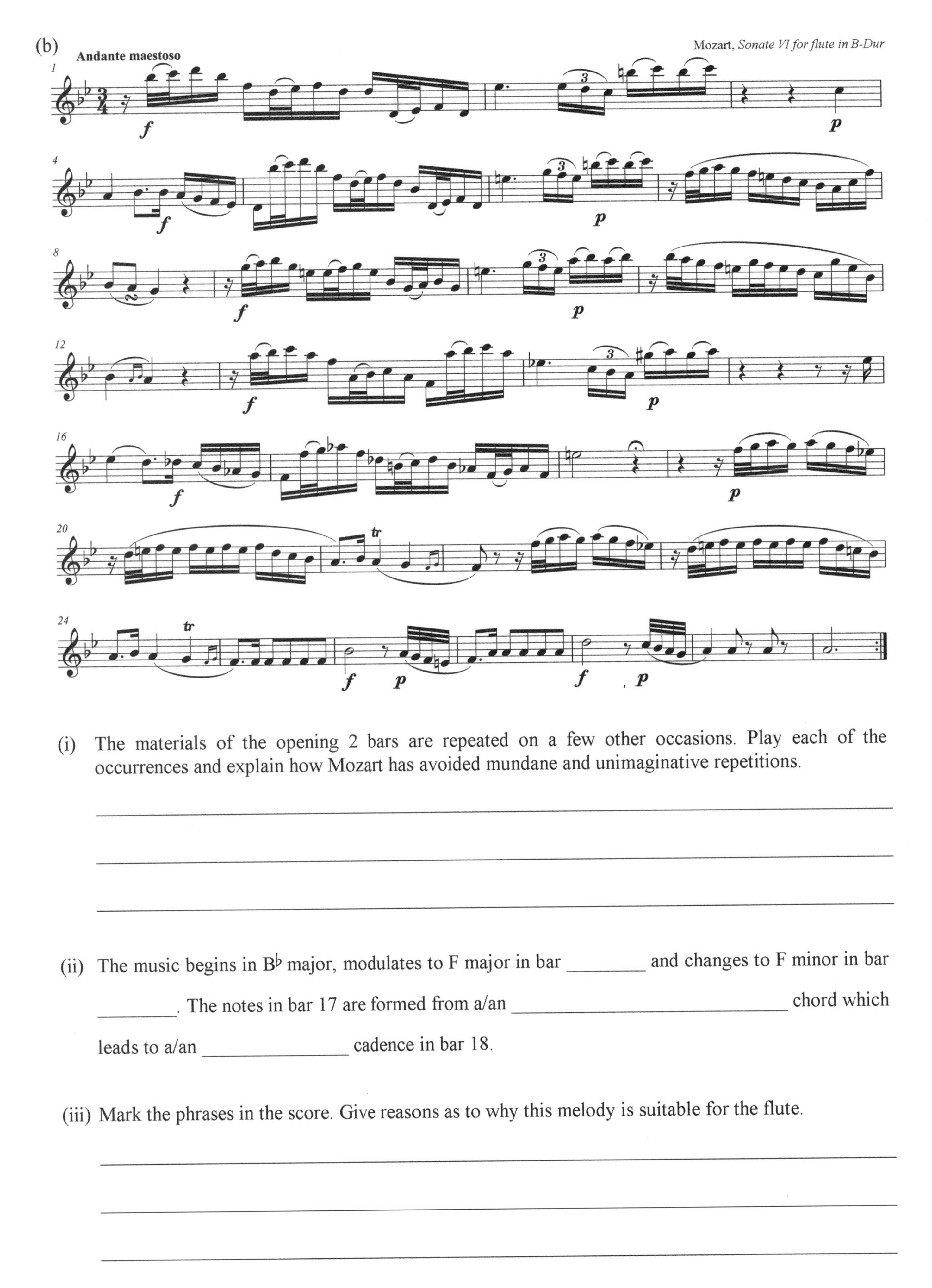

(i) The materials of the opening 2 bars are repeated on a few other occasions. Play each of the occurrences and explain how Mozart has avoided mundane and unimaginative repetitions.

____

____

____

(ii) The music begins in B♭ major, modulates to F major in bar ________ and changes to F minor in bar ________. The notes in bar 17 are formed from a/an ______________________________ chord which leads to a/an ______________ cadence in bar 18.

(iii) Mark the phrases in the score. Give reasons as to why this melody is suitable for the flute.

____

____

____

(c) Play the opening theme and then Variation I of the extract below. Compare the similarities and differences. Pay careful attention as to how the continuous triplet figures are derived and how melodic interest is created.

22. Compose a melody of not less than 12 bars using each of the given openings and for the specified unaccompanied instrument. Continue in the same style and include appropriate performance directions. Write each complete melody on the staves provided.

(a) VIOLIN

(b) FLUTE

(c) CELLO

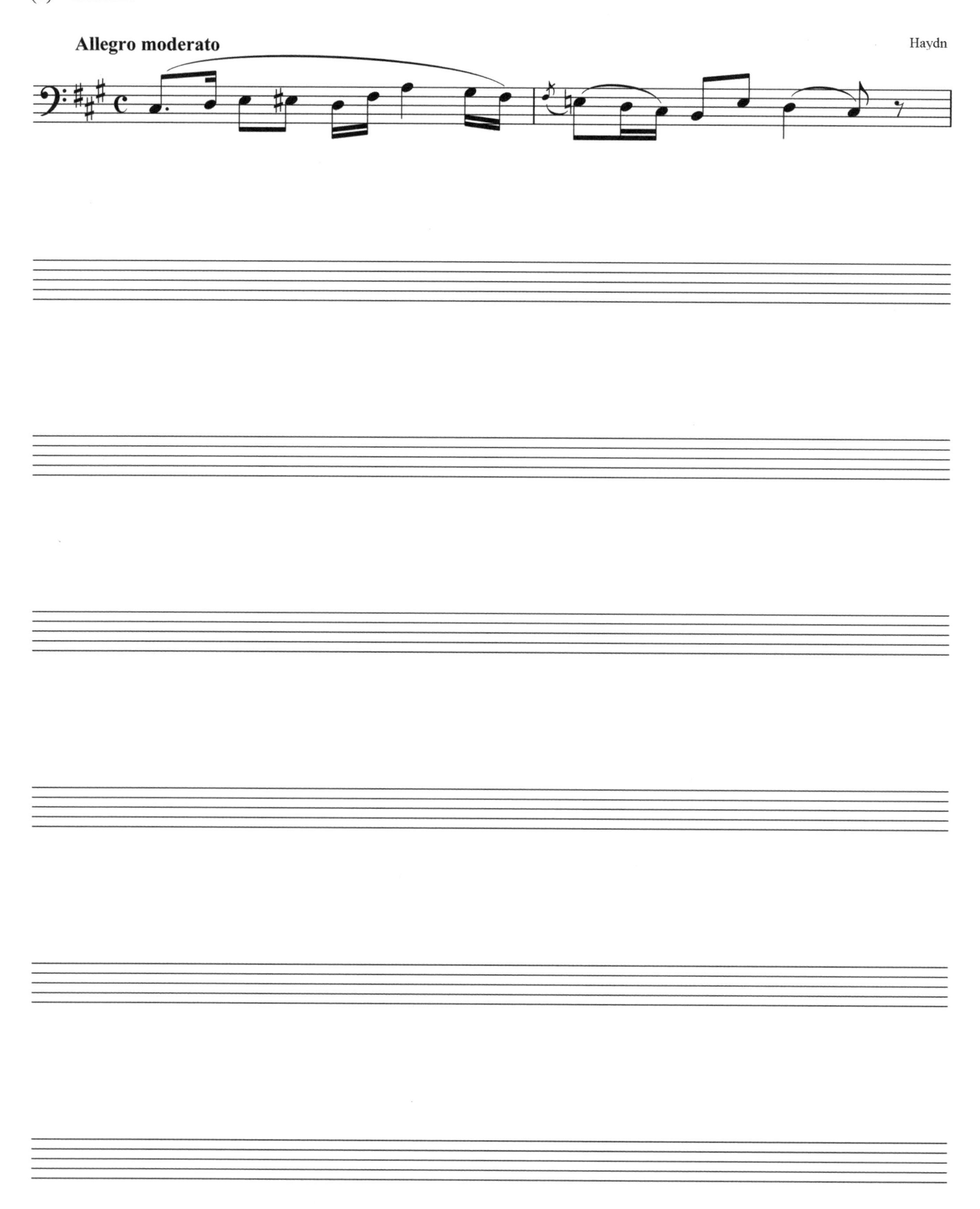

Melodic Writing in the 19th Century

Most melodies of the 19th century are less effective if played unaccompanied as they form the musical materials originally designed to be part of more complex musical textures. Nevertheless, most melodic compositions are developed and constructed, based on the opening materials. The example below illustrates this phenomenon.

Charles Gounod, *Meditation "Ave Maria" for cello & piano*

23. Study the 19th century melodies that follow and observe how musical coherence, contrast and continuity are achieved.

(a) CLARINET

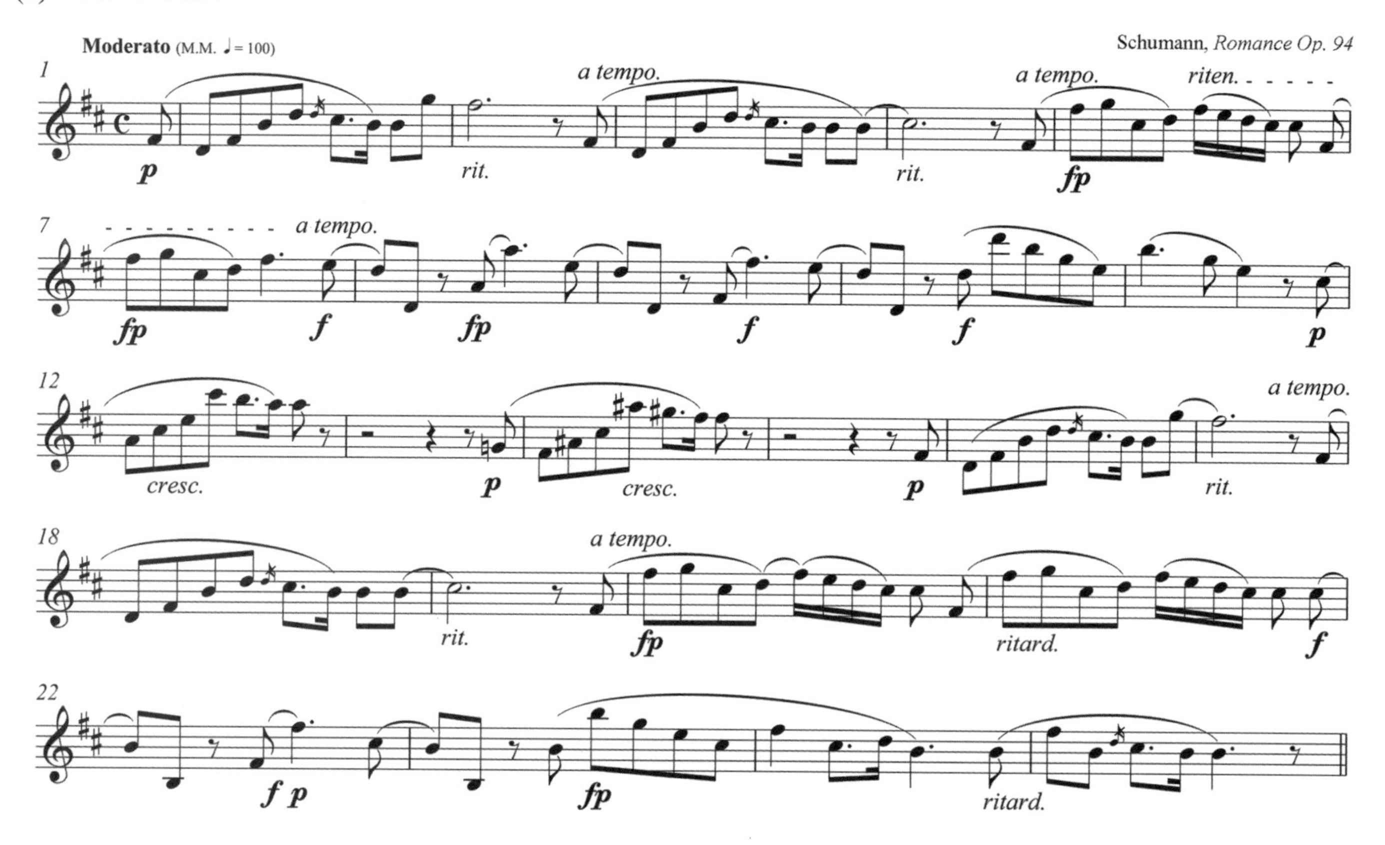

Mark out the phrases in the melody above and then discuss the points of interest below.

(i) Study the triadic nature of the opening bar and discuss its use in the extract.

(ii) Where does the second phrase begin? From where does it derive its materials?

(iii) Comment on the use of melodic material from bar 14 to the end of the extract.

(b) This extract is a continuation of the melody on the previous page. Discuss the difference in the treatment of this new section and make notes on the various aspects suggested below.

(i) In what key does the passage begin? Discuss the use of accidentals and whether modulations are implied.

(ii) Discuss the rhythmic and melodic organisation of this continuation and explain how it relates to the previous section.

(c) VIOLIN

Sibelius, *Serenade for Violin Op. 74 No. 4*

(i) Describe some features found in this melody which strike which you as predominantly different from the few examples quoted earlier.

____

____

____

____

(ii) What tempo or mode of expression do you think would be appropriate for the performance of this work?

____

____

____

____

(iii) From where does this melody derive its materials? Elaborate on the various means of melodic development.

____

____

____

____

(iv) This melody has a modal flavour. Mark out the phrases and give an account of the overall construction, paying attention to the melodic contour, range of notes used and rhythmic effects generated.

____

____

____

____

24. Compose a melody of not less than 12 bars using each of the given openings. Continue in the suggested styles and include appropriate performance directions. Write each complete melody on the staves provided.

(a) CELLO

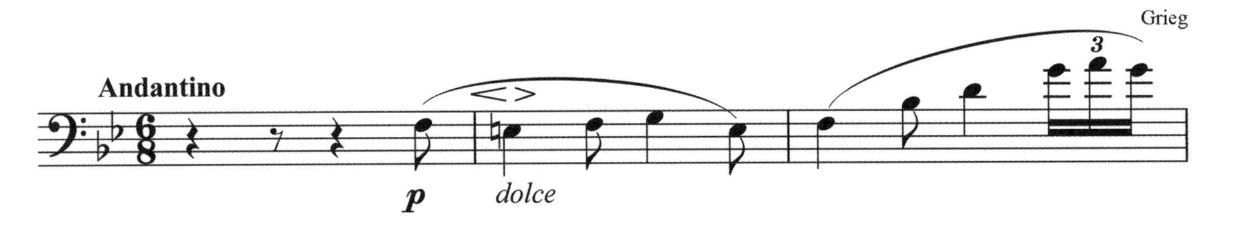

(b) BASSOON

(c) OBOE

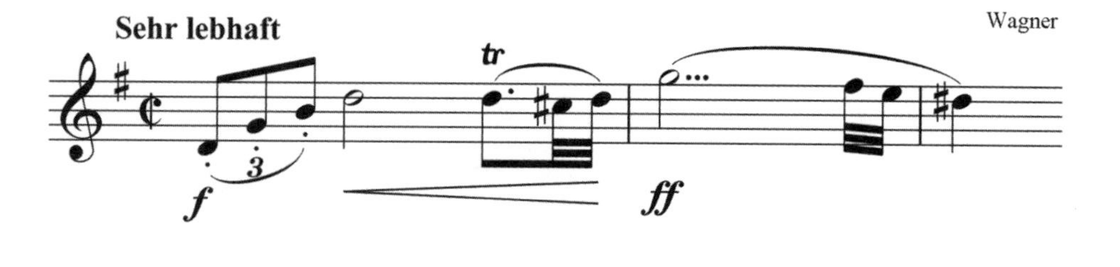

Modern Compositional Techniques

The study of modern works is further explored at Grade 8 with reference to more intricate melodic compositional techniques. One of the most distinctive modern developments is the eventual negation of tonality – a revolution in the ever-widening exploration of the expressive resources of chromaticism. Though non tonal music may not have gained universal acceptance, the search for new techniques of composition have been of great interest for composers of the century. In the study examples that follow, students will benefit from the insights into some of the innovations that have made their mark in the history of Western music.

Musical Examples

(a) **Melodies based on chord shapes**

In the opening bars, despite the absence of a key-signature, the ascending arpeggios of the first three bars lead to two different chords.

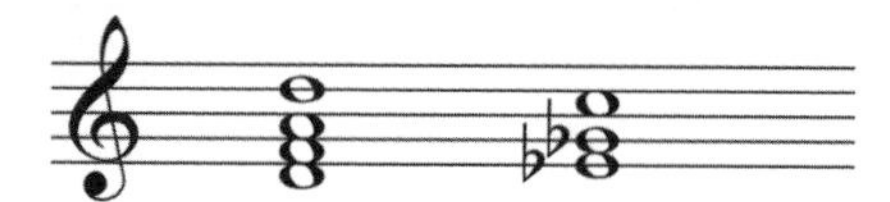

In the continuation, a harmonic framework can be traced within the next three bars which is a sequence based on two chords.

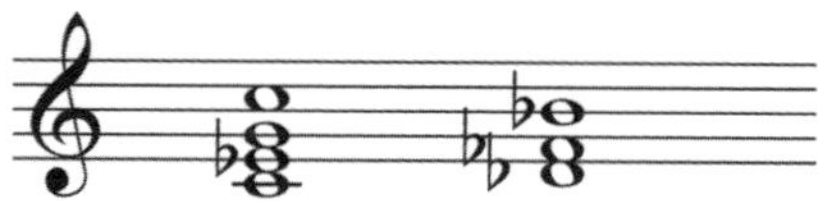

The subsequent four bars form another phrase, bringing the phrase structure of **C** to (3 + 3 + 4). **D** ushers in contrasting materials with the phrase lengths (2 + 2 + 3). The concluding **E** section recapitulates the opening materials of **C** .

(b) The revival of modality

Resting on Aeolian modality, the charm of this melody is enhanced by parallel harmonies (not printed here). In the music of Debussy, the use of the pentatonic scale, whole tone scale, along with unresolved harmonies result in music which negates traditional tonality. The effect becomes impressionistic, creating a sense of vagueness with modernity.

(c) Tonal centres within passages of free tonality

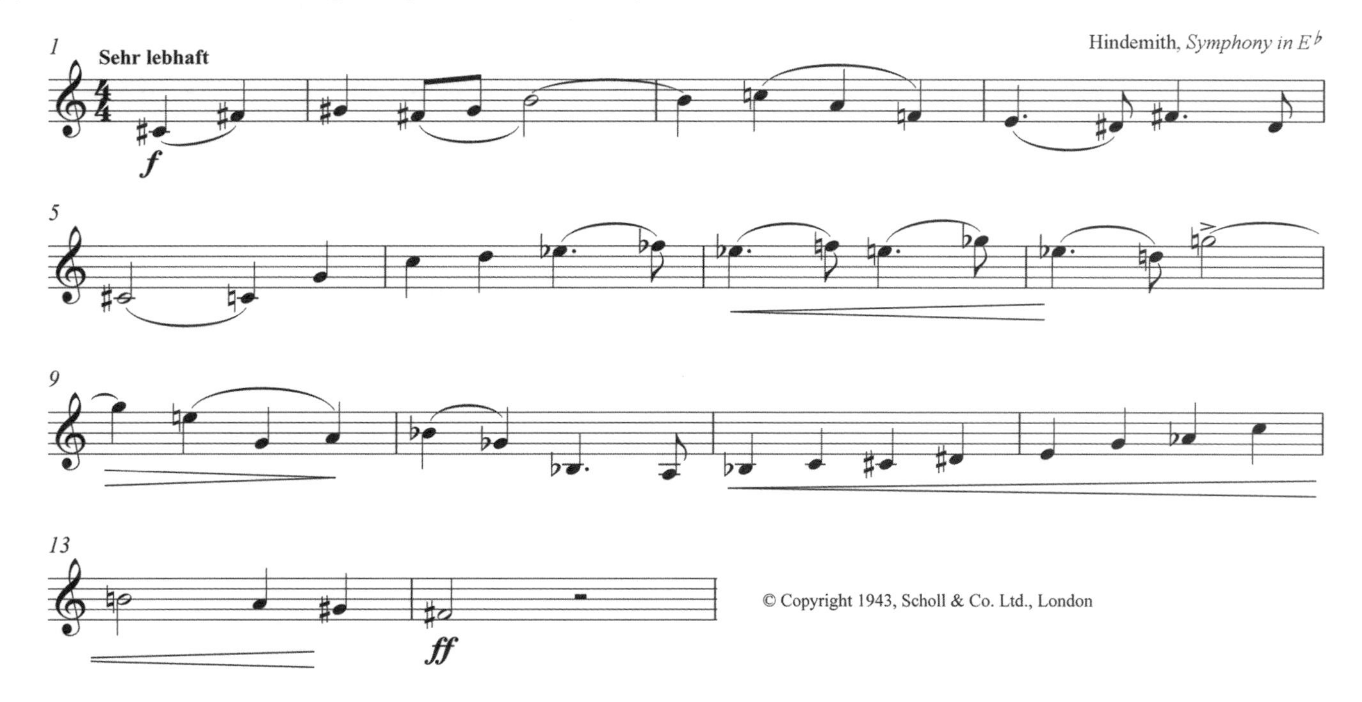

The tonal centre F♯ is established at the beginning and ends with a clear cadence on that note. On the whole, the passage is written in free tonality with all the 12 notes of the chromatic scale utilised within the 12 bars. The composer attains the first climax effectively at bar 7 and subsequently at the end. Instead of a random choice of notes, the melody achieves a high degree of conviction through its logical contour and construction.

(d) Atonality

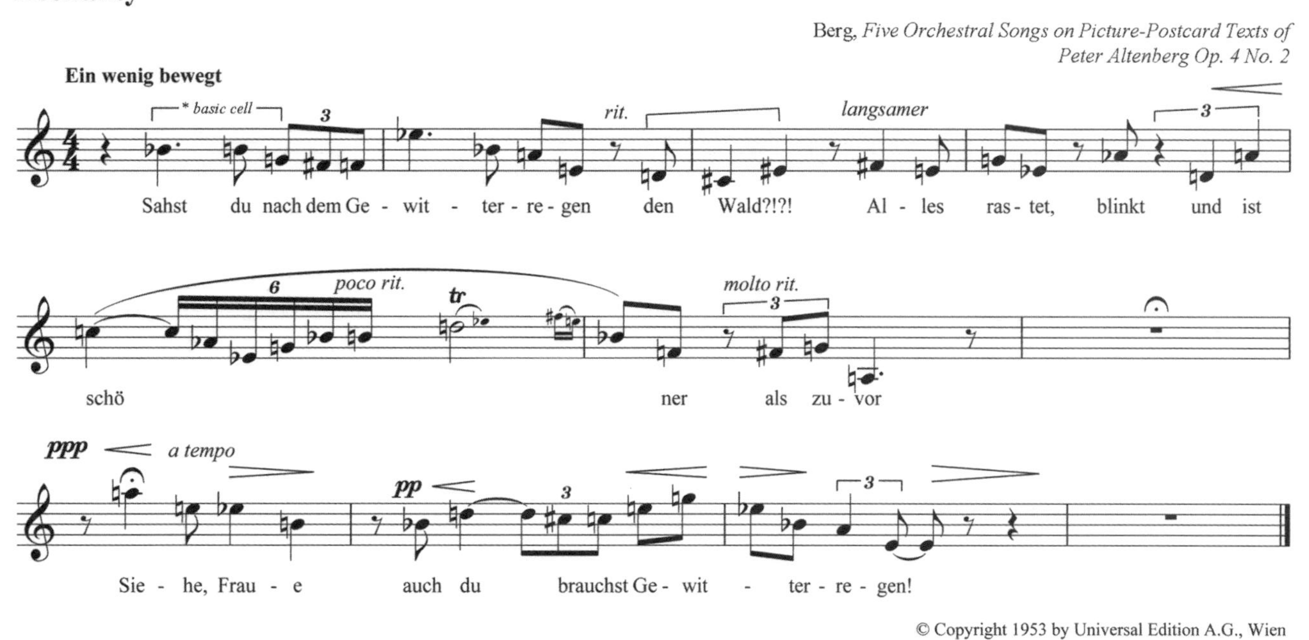

In the example above, the atonal song results from the successive and overlapping transpositions of a *single intervallic cell, a major 3rd and a semitone in the opposite direction.

(e) **Serialism**

The influence of Schoenberg and his followers has been enormous. More potent is the technique of the twelve tone series, known as *serialism*, whereby the pitch relationships of a work are based on a predetermined order of notes from the chromatic scale. (See *Musical Forms & Terms*)

Below is the Violin I part from Berg's Lyric Suite (1926). It is written for a string quartet using the serial technique. Notice the fragmented character of the music, very detailed dynamic markings and bow marks (bars 13-14).

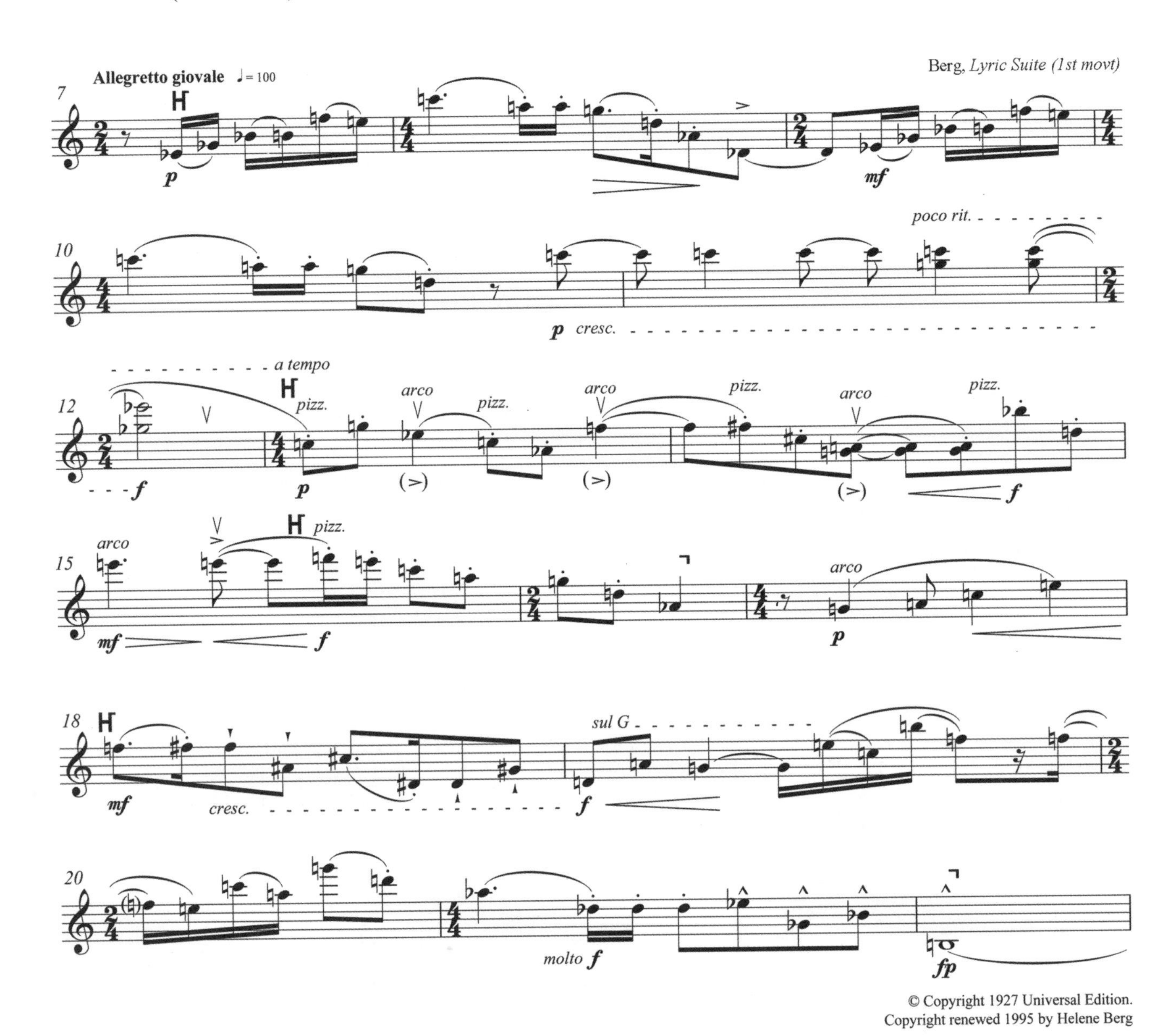

(f) **Other innovations**

One of Elliot Carter's important contributions has been to develop a new approach to changes in tempo and rhythm among instruments in a continuous movement. He devised a technique which he called "tempo modulation". This means that an individual instrumental part may speed up or slow down while others remain at the same tempo, accelerate or decelerate. In the Violin I part of the *String Quartet No. 2*, Carter indicated in his preface that the player should display not only its individualized tempo and rhythm but also its character – sometimes precise, at other times free, fantastic and virtuosic.

Carter, *String Quartet No. 2*

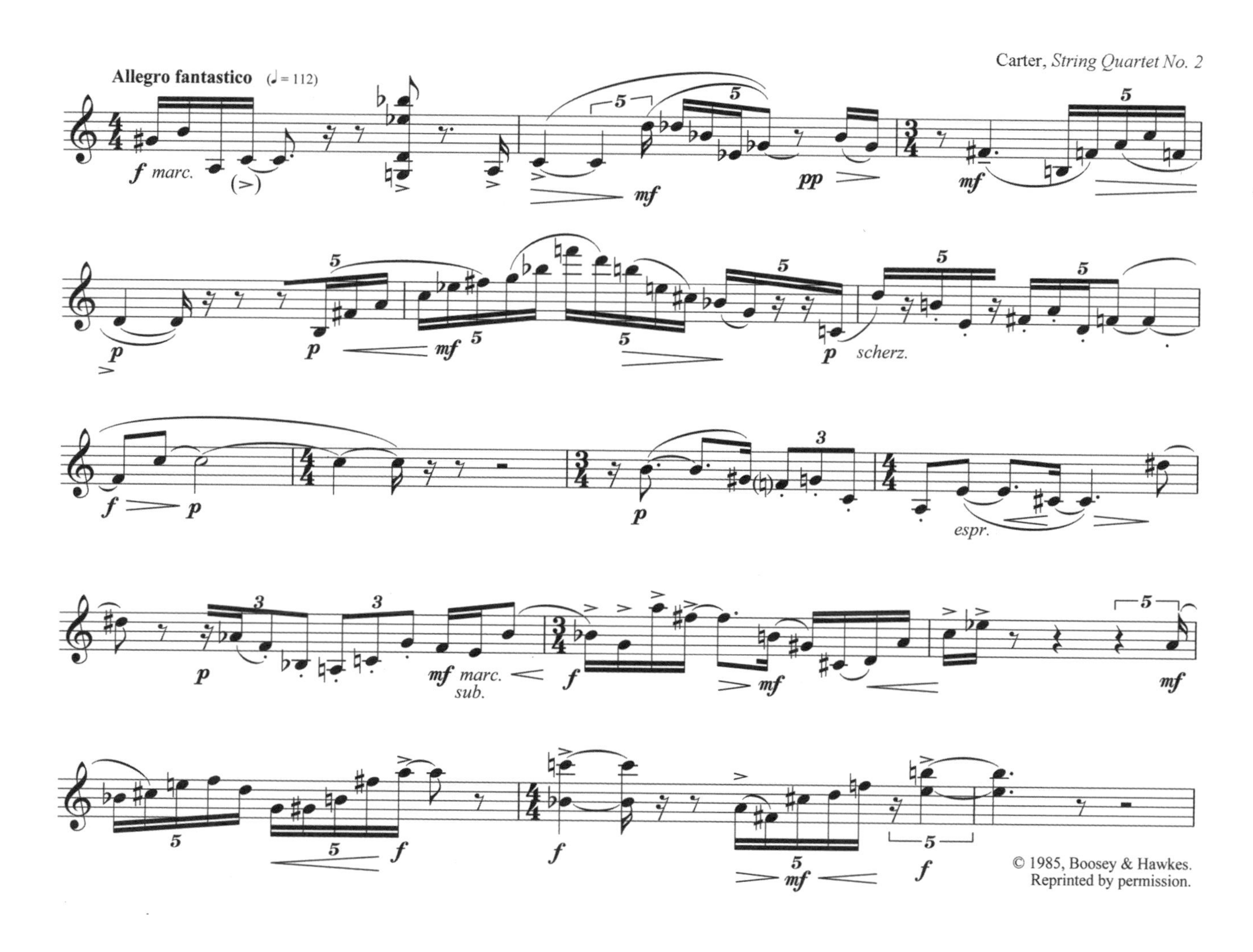

25. Continue the following opening to make a short piece of not less than 12 bars in the style of a fanfare for solo trumpet. Observe the melodic intervals and introduce chromatic notes to avoid any suggestion of major or minor tonality.

26. Continue the melody to form an Elegy for oboe of up to 16 bars. Introduce chromaticism but ensure that the piece projects C as its tonal centre.

27. In about 12 bars, make a short serial composition for bassoon using the following note-row and opening:

28. Continue the following opening for a further 12 to 20 bars to form an elegy for the oboe. Create an expressive, cadenza-like passage in the middle before concluding your composition.

OBOE

29. Compose a complete melody of 12 to 20 bars using the opening below for unaccompanied violin. Continue in the same style and include performance directions.

VIOLIN

Section V

Score-Reading & Analysis

Score Reading & Analysis

Following the revised theory syllabus from 1999, short structured questions in the analysis section require students to show a good knowledge and understanding of musical scores. Similar to Grades 6 and 7, the examination paper contains two extracts of music: one scored for 1 to 4 performers and the other for 5 or more performers, possibly up to a large orchestra including chorus and soloists. The questions asked will be based on the following:

(i) **Harmony**
- To identify the *prevailing key* and analyse the chords in relation to it. The student should be familiar with features and qualities of the *diminished 7th, secondary dominants, Neapolitan 6th, augmented 6th, borrowed* and *altered* versions of chords, and their functions.
- To identify chromaticism, and the use of non-harmony notes.

(ii) **Musical Terms**
- To grasp, understand and use musical terms and jargons in the contexts in which they occur, including the genre, foreign terms and to explain or discuss characteristics associated with various musical styles and works.

(iii) **Phrasing, Form and Structure**
- To show an understanding of musical construction, with the ability to recognize the *form* or section of which the extract is taken from and to discuss its significance in relation to the movement or work as a whole.

(iv) **Musical History and Repertory**
- To identify the characteristic features of a particular composer.
- To discuss features of the music that illustrate a particular period of composition or style.
- To list other genres, composers or titles of works related to the one given.

(v) **Orchestration and Instrumentation**
- To write out at concert pitch the sounding notes for transposing instruments; or to write out from the sounding pitches the written notes as they would appear for transposing instruments.
- To discuss the use of special effects intended by the composer.
- To comment on the use of instruments, their articulation, timbre, and overall mood created with reference to the use of dynamics and expression marks.

It is of great importance that listening and analytical skills, including score-reading and reading of relevant materials become part of the student's musical education. A suggested reading list is provided on page 117.

Musical Analysis

The analysis questions in the examination often require students to make comments and mark or indicate their observations on the musical extracts. They will also be required to compare various sections of the extract(s) and identify the predominant musical features. In the study of analysis, the main areas of concern are outlined below.

Motif, Phrase Structure and Form

The student needs to identify and explain, by using bar numbers, how a melodic or rhythmic motif is being developed or used in the extract. Phrases need to be marked and may be described in terms of length (e.g. 4-bars, 8-bars), and whether they are regular or irregular and balanced or unbalanced. A predominant form or structure may prevail, such as *binary*, *ternary*, *rondo* or *sonata form*.

Melodic treatment and features to be mentioned include *repetitions*, *sequences*, *imitations*, *melodic extensions*, *inversions* and *variations*. Keys, modulations, cadences or the lack of such elements lead to the need to identify other compositional devices and techniques, such as the *whole tone scale*, *pentatonic scale*, *atonality* and *serialism*.

Rhythmic features often include the types of note values used, any unusual grouping of notes and how rhythmic variety is achieved. Irregularities in the extract(s) may include *changing meter*, use of *syncopation*, *hemiola*, *cross rhythms*, *shifted accents* and *polyrhythms*.

Texture and Timbre

The understanding of texture requires the student to examine the *number of parts* (instrumental or vocal), the dynamics and types or groups of instruments employed. Often, texture can be described as *homophonic, polyphonic, multi-tier, thick* or *thin, sparse* or *massive*. Other possible descriptions include *transparent, chordal* and even *pointilistic.*

Timbre is closely related to texture and instrumentation. It refers to the various tone colours produced in different musical contexts. Soft dynamics, the use of high notes and limited instruments usually suggest a thin, sometimes transparent texture. The use of mutes or tremolos in strings can create a special timbre typical of impressionistic works. On the other hand, the use of brass instruments, notes of the lower register and chordal passages usually suggest a thick and often dense texture. A powerful timbre can be created by the heightened use of trumpets, trombones and added tubas.

Instrumentation

A discussion on instrumentation is beyond the scope of this book and has to be presented in a different context as styles and practices vary among composers in the different periods. A greater and broader understanding on the subject require further reading on orchestration and its development. Primarily, different combinations of instruments produce different effects. Special playing techniques, such as the use of glissando, pizzicato, double and triple stops, stopped horns, switching of pitch instruments and the treatment of percussion instruments are in many ways critical to the overall timbre, mood and character portrayed.

Character and mood

The mood and character of a work is often suggested by a combination of factors, including dynamics, instrumentation, rhythm, melody and texture. A climax may be developed over a long stretch or driven to its peak within a few bars. Emotions are often suggested, whether they are feelings of assured tranquility, restrained passion, or mere frantic anxiety. A word list is presented here to assist students with their description. Alternatively, you may think of the instruments or musical features that can possibly conjure the effects.

a) ***Quick pieces***

fast and lively	dramatic	proclaimatory
highly spirited	pompous	exuberant
gay and merry	thunderous	exclamatory
joyous	boisterous	dance-like
energetic	buzzing	ceremonial
exciting	comical	marching style
fiery	joking	delightful
with propelling momentum	anxious	frantic

b) ***Slow and loud/soft pieces***

slow	poignant	nocturnal
solemn	menacing	tranquil
grave	mysterious	warm
sad	foreboding	whispering
grievous	threatening	trembling
ponderous	whimsy	vibrating
hesitant	light	shivering
stagnant	soothing	shimmering

References and Recommended Reading List

Donald Jay Grout, *A History of Western Music (5th Edition)*
(USA: W.W. NORTON 1996)

Robert P. Morgan (ed), *Anthology of Twentieth Century Music*
(USA: W.W. NORTON 1992)

Walter Piston & Mark Devoto, *Harmony (Revised Ed)*
(YORKSHIRE: W.W. NORTON 1981)

Eric Taylor, *The AB Guide to Music Theory, Part II*
(LONDON: ABRSM 1991)

Josephine Koh, *Musical Forms and Terms*
(SINGAPORE: WELLS MUSIC PUBLISHERS 2007)

Peter Aston & Julian Webb, *Music Theory in Practice*
(LONDON: ABRSM 1993)

Reginald Smith Brindle, *The New Music: The Avante Garde since 1945*
(USA: OXFORD 1987)

Claude V. Palisca (ed), *Norton Anthology of Western Music: Classic to Modern*
(USA: W.W NORTON 1996)

Vincent Persichetti, *Twentieth Century Harmony: Creative Aspects and Practice*
(LONDON: FABER 1978)

Samuel Adler, *The Study of Orchestration (2nd Edition)*
(USA: W.W. NORTON 1989)

Stanley Sadie (ed), *The New Grove Dictionary of Music and Musicians*
(LONDON: MACMILLAN 1980)

Denes Agay, *Teaching Piano, Volume II*
(USA: YORKTOWN 1981)

Paul Griffiths, *Modern Music and After, Directions since 1945*
(USA: OXFORD UNIVERSITY PRESS 1995)

Rimsky-Korsakov, *Principles of Orchestration*
(USA: DOVER 1964)

Antony Hopkins, *Understanding Music*
(LONDON: DENT 1979)

Anna Butterworth, *Harmony in Practice*
(LONDON: ABRSM 1999)

30. Study the two variations on the opposite page and then answer the questions that follow.

(a) What is the name given to each of the melodic decoration marked W, X, Y and Z in the score?

W (bar 4) ______________________

X (bar 5) ______________________

Y (bar 13) ______________________

Z (bar 14) ______________________

(b) Write out the top line of the right hand part of bar 2 and bar 14 (1st half) as you think they should be played.

bar 2

bar 14 (1st half)

(c) What is the complete technical term used to describe bars 7 and 8 as compared to bars 5 and 6?

____

(d) Complete the statements below:

(i) Each of the variation is in itself, in simple __________ form. The first phrase is ______ bars in length with the __________ phrase being a __________ of the first phrase.

(ii) The passage is in the key of __________. There is a temporary modulation to __________ at bars 5 - 6 and bars 17 - 18.

(iii) The melodic notes of bars 1 and 2 can be heard in the __________ part of bars 13 and 14. Similarly the melodic notes of bars 5 to 9 are heard in the __________ part of bars ______ to ______.

(e) Suggest two other differences between Variation II and Variation III.

1. ______________________

2. ______________________

(f) Name a possible composer for the work. Composer: ______________________

1
VAR. II
W
p
5
f
X
p
f
p
9
f
p
13
VAR. III
Y
tr
Z
3
17
21
tr

31. Study the extract printed opposite from Faure's Nocturne No. 4, then answer the following questions.

(a) Explain the following terms:

(i) **Andante molto moderato** ____________________

(ii) *poco a poco cresc.* ____________________

(iii) *dolce e cantabile* ____________________

(iv) *a tempo* ____________________

(b) Mark clearly in the score, using the appropriate capital letter for identification, one example of each of the following. Also give the bar numbers of your answers.

A a cross rhythm effect. Bar ______

B an appoggiatura found in the melody. Bar ______

C a bar which contains a dominant 7th and a diminished 7th chord. Bar ______

D a chromatic scale found in an inner part. Bar ______

E an augmented chord found within the first 10 bars. Bar ______

(c) Compare bars 12 to 15 with bars 1 to 4 and identify three differences.

1. ____________________

2. ____________________

3. ____________________

(d) Identify and describe the chords marked with a *⎣_⎦ in the passage. Indicate the chords as major, minor, diminished or augmented. The prevailing key must be shown in each case.

1. ____________________ Key: __________

2. ____________________ Key: __________

3. ____________________ Key: __________

4. ____________________ Key: __________

(e) Complete the following statements.

(i) Each melodic phrase is _______ bars long except for bar 11 which forms a/an ______________.

(ii) Apart from the tempo, the nocturnal effect of the piece is brought about by ________________

____

____

Nocturne No. 4 Op. 36

Andante molto moderato
(♩ = 56)
dolce
1 *
poco
poco
cresc.
mf
p
2 *
3 *
pp
poco rit.
a tempo
dolce e cantabile
4 *

32. Study the extract printed opposite and answer the following questions.

(a) Mark clearly in the score, using the appropriate capital letter for identification, one example of each of the following. Also give the bar numbers of your answers

A a 9 - 8 suspension in the tonic key. Bar ______

B an accented passing note in the bass line. Bar ______

C a chromatic auxiliary note in a string part. Bar ______

D a tierce de picardie. Bar ______

E a decorated version of a 7 - 6 suspension. Bar ______

(b) Mark out the phrases of the passage by using a ┌──────┐ above the part of the flauto traverso, then complete the statement below.

(i) The first modulation occurs at bar _______ to the key of ________________. A few bars later it modulates to _______________. A temporary modulation to ________________ occurs at bars 16-17 before returning to the tonic key.

(ii) The subject is first heard in the ____________________ and ____________________. At bar _______, an imitation at a 3rd below occurs in the ____________________ and ____________________ parts. At bar 10, the subject is heard in the ____________________ and at bar 16 it is heard again in the ____________________ and ____________________.

(iii) Underline the word that describes the texture of the extract.

Polyphonic Monodic Homophonic Multi-tier

(c) Name the chords marked * in bars 4 and 9.

bar 4 _______________ chord, _______________ position/inversion in the key of ________________.

bar 9 ________________________________

(d) Name a possible composer and the type of work the extract is taken from. Give three reasons that would support your answer.

Composer: ______________________ Type of work: ______________________

Reasons:

1. ____

2. ____

3. ____

Alla breve
Flauto traverso
Violino concertato
Violino I
Violino II
Viola
Violoncello e Violone
Cembalo concertato
tr
Fl.
V.c.
Vl.
Vla.
Vc.e Vne.
C.

13
Fl.
V.c.
Vl.
Vla.
Vc.e
Vne.
C.
tr
19
Fl.
V.c.
Vl.
Vla.
Vc.e
Vne.
C.

33. Study the opening extract from Brahm's 4th Symphony in E minor, Op. 98, then answer the questions below.

(a) Mark clearly in the score, using the appropriate capital letter for identification, one example of each of the following that occurs from bars 10 to the end of the extract.

A an augmented French 6th chord, found after the first 10 bars. Bar ______

B a passing note in a string part. Bar ______

C a dominant 9th chord forming a perfect cadence in E minor. Bar ______

D a diminished 7th chord on G♯. Bar ______

E a one-bar melodic sequence at a 3rd below. Bar ______

(b) How should the notes of the woodwind parts in the opening bars be articulated?

____

(c) Circle the term which best describes the musical effect between the violins and the woodwind instruments in bars 1 to 5.

Tonal Sequence   Canon   Augmentation   Counterpoint

(d) Complete the statements below:

A tonic pedal occurs in the ________________ and ________________ from bars _____ to _____.

A similar occurrence later can be found in the ________________ from bars _____ to _____.

(e) Rewrite the clarinet parts at concert pitch from bars 5 to 7.

(f) Which of the following statements about the extract are true? Answer TRUE or UNTRUE in each case.

(i) The flutes double the clarinets at an octave above throughout. ________________

(ii) The double bass plays the same note as the first note of the cello in each bar. ________________

(iii) All tied notes used in the passage are not suspensions. ________________

(iv) Non-harmony notes only begin to appear from bar 9. ________________

(v) Other than the violins, non of the other string instruments has melodic roles. ________________

Johannes Brahms, *Op. 98*

10
Fl.
Kl.
Fg.
Hrn. (C)
Vl.
Br.
Vc.
Kb.
15
Hb.
(E)
Hrn.
(C)
Vc. n. Kb.
Bassi
leggiero

34. Study the extract taken from a tone poem, then answer the questions that follow.

(a) Explain the following terms.

(i) 1.2.zu 2 ______________________________

(ii) *hervortretend* ______________________________

(iii) *get.* ______________________________

(iv) *espr.* ______________________________

(b) Write out the horn parts of bar 1 as they would sound at concert pitch.

(c) Comment on the role of the harps. What makes them sound so distinct in this passage?

____

____

(d) Explain and describe how the 1st violins should play the first bar.

____

____

(e) In what key(s) do you think the clarinets are pitched? Give your reasons.

Pitched in: ____________. Reason: ______________________________

____

(f) Underline the most likely composer of the extract and give three reasons for your choice.

Chopin Schumann Richard Strauss Benjamin Britten Debussy

Reasons:

1. ______________________________

2. ______________________________

3. ______________________________

Fl.
cresc.
Hob.
E.H.
1.2.zy 2
hervortretend
cresc.
Kl.
cresc.
cresc.
B.-Kl.
mf espr.
cresc.
Fg.
K.-Fg.
1.2.3.
espr.
K.-Fg.
1.2.
Hr. (F)
p hervortretend
cresc.
7.8.
2.4.
espr.
zu 2
5.6.
T.-Tb.
7.8.
mf espr.
cresc.
Pk.
1.Hrf.
2.Hrf.
Vl.
get.
arco.
cresc.
cresc.
Br.
get.
Vc.
espr.
cresc.
Kb.

35. The following extract is taken from *Prayers of Kierkegaard for Mixed Chorus, Soprano Solo and Orchestra with Incidental Tenor Solo, Alto Solo Ad Libitum* by Samuel Barber. Study it and then answer the questions that follow.

(a) Explain the following terms that are used to indicate how the opening passage is to be sung by the whole chorus.

(i) a capella ______________________________

(ii) ***pp*** *legatissimo* ______________________________

(iii) Grave and remote ______________________________

(iv) ♩= 56 ______________________________

(b) Underline the word that best describes the opening male chorus melody from bars 1 to 13.

Bitonal Atonal Modal Polytonal

(c) Mark clearly on the score, using the appropriate capital letter for identification, one example of each of the following. Also give the bar numbers of your answers.

In Extract I

A tenor and basses singing in unison. Bar ______

In Extract II

B tremolo played as a double stop. Bar ______

C the tenor part of the 1st chorus doubled by a wind instrument. Bar ______

D imitation of the soprano part of the 1st chorus in an instrumental part. Bar ______

E modified repetition of the opening piccolo melody. Bar ______

(d) Write out the English Horn part of Extract II, bars 19-20 as it would sound at concert pitch. Do not use any key signature.

English Horn at concert pitch

(e) Name four ways in which the composer creates contrast between *Extract I* and *Extract II*.

1. ______________________________

2. ______________________________

3. ______________________________

4. ______________________________

EXTRACT I

Grave and remote ♩= 56
pp legatissimo
Male Chorus
a capella *
O Thou who art un - change - a - ble, whom noth - ing chang - es, May we find our rest and re -
Male Chorus
main at rest in thee un - chang - ing. Thou art moved and moved in in - fi - nite love by all things: the
Male Chorus
need of a spar - row, e - ven this moves thee and what we scarce - ly see, a hu - man sigh,
poco allarg.
2
Moderato ♩= 56
a tempo
dolce
Fl.
Ob.
Cl.(A)
B.Cl.
Bsn.
Hn.
Trb.
Ten.
this moves Thee, O in - fi - nite Love!
Bass
this moves Thee, O in - fi - nite Love!
poco allarg.
Moderato ♩= 56
Vln.
Vla.
Vc.
Cb.

EXTRACT II

18 Beginning a new and more intense cresc., moving ahead
Picc.
Fl.
Ob.
Eng.Hn
Cl.
B.Cl.
Bsn.
Hn.
Tuba
Timp
Perc.
Harp
Piano
S
A
I
T
B
S
A
II
T
B
Vln
I
II
Vla.
Vc.
Cb.
mp espr.
mf espr.
sempre marc.
poco f espr.
Trgl.
good,
when Thou dost of - fer us,
Thou dost of - fer us the high - est good,
When Thou dost of - fer us the high - est
Beginning a new and more intense cresc.
moving gradually ahead
grazioso
pizz.
arco
sf poco
p sub.

Theory Assignments

Date	Assignments	Corrections	Remarks

Theory Assignments

Date	Assignments	Corrections	Remarks

Best-Selling Titles

Quick Study Practice for Piano Diploma Exams
by Josephine Koh

Quick Study Practice for Piano Diploma Students contains selected piano works that aim to help students acquire the skills they need to meet the basic requirements of Quick Study and to demonstrate the musicianship expected of a convincing performance. Informative study points are provided as a useful guide which may be referred to prior or after having played the pieces. It is a recommended approach to assist students to attain success in their examinations.

Scales & Arpeggios for Piano Grade 8
Fingering & Tonality Method
by Josephine Koh

Presented in an exciting and fresh form, learning and playing rudimentary scales will never be the same again. The Fingering and Tonality Method adopts both an aural and visual approaches which are organized to optimize the learning process. Based on the ABRSM piano exam syllabus, the tonality concept is emphasized to facilitate reflective mastery of all scales and arpeggios.

Available from Grades 6 to 8.

Teachers' Choice Grades 8
Piano Examination Pieces 2007-2008
Edited and Annotated by Josephine Koh

A refreshing new publication which comprises popular and alternative works from the ABRSM Piano Examination syllabus. These pieces are specially selected to provide students with a comprehensive and varied repertoire. Meticulously fingered and edited, *Teachers' Choice* offers teachers and students alike with added performance and teaching directions. Scores in *Teachers' Choice* are beautifully set and annotated for excellent reading.

Available from Grades 6 to 8.